SCHOLASTIC

100
LITERACY
HOMEWORK
ACTIVITIES

- Stand-alone homework sheets
- Fits with any programme
- Easy to use

YEAR 5

Scottish Primary 6

Chris Webster

ACKNOWLEDGEMENTS

Published by Scholastic Ltd,
Villiers House,
Clarendon Avenue,
Leamington Spa,
Warwickshire CV32 5PR

© 2001 Scholastic Ltd
Text © Chris Webster 2001

Printed by Bell & Bain Ltd, Glasgow

1 2 3 4 5 6 7 8 9   6 7 8 9 0

AUTHORS
Chris Webster

EDITORIAL & DESIGN
Crystal Presentations Ltd

COVER DESIGN
Joy Monkhouse

ILLUSTRATOR
Phil Garner

British Library Cataloguing-in-Publication Data
A catalogue record for this book is available from the British Library.

ISBN 0-439-94485-6
ISBN 978-0439-94485-4

The publishers gratefully acknowledge permission to reproduce the following copyright material:

Carlton Books Limited for the use of 'Away from it All' by Ogden Nash from *Candy is Dandy: The Best of Ogden Nash* with an introduction by Anthony Burgess © 1994, Odgen Nash (1994, Andre Deutsch).
David Higham Associates for the use of 'Little spider' by Mervyn Peake from *A Book of Nonsense* by Mervyn Peake © 1972, Mervyn Peake (1972, Peter Owen).
David Higham Associates for the use of an extract from *George's Marvellous Medicine* by Roald Dahl © 1982, Roald Dahl (1982, Puffin).
Gerald Duckworth & Co Limited for the use of 'Overheard on a saltmarsh' by Harold Monro from *Collected Poems* by Harold Monro © 1970, Harold Monro (1970, Gerald Duckworth & Co Limited).
Hachette Children's Books for the use of an extract from *Princess by Mistake* by Penelope Lively © 1993, Penelope Lively (1993, Hodder Wayland).
HarperCollins Publishers for the use of an extract from *Duckula and the Ghost Train* by John Broadhead © 1988, John Broadhead (1988, Collins).
Horwitz Martin Education for the use of an extract 'The Haunted House' from *Read Well 4* by Gordon Winch and Gregory Blaxell © 1996, Gordon Winch and Gregory Blaxell (1996, Horwitz Martin Education).
Orion Publishing Group Limited for the use of an extract from *The Borrowers* by Mary Norton © 1952, Mary Norton (1952, J M Dent).
Jack Prelutsky for the use of 'Wild witches' ball' by Jack Prelutsky from *Witches Poems* edited by Daisy Wallace © 1976, Jack Prelutsky (1976, Holiday House).
Sharland Organisation for the use of an extract from *Super Gran Rules OK!* by Forrest Wilson © 1984, Forrest Wilson (1984, Puffin).
Kit Wright for the use of 'My dad, your dad' by Kit Wright from *Rabbiting On* by Kit Wright © 1978, Kit Wright (1978, Collins).
Extracts from the National Literacy Strategy © Crown copyright. Reproduced under the terms of HMSO Guidance Note 8.

Every effort has been made to trace copyright holders. The publishers apologise for any inadvertent omissions.

100 Literacy Homework Activities: Year 5

100 Literacy Homework Activities: Year 5

Using the books

The activities in each book are organised by term, then by word-, sentence- and text-level focus and, finally, by specific National Literacy Strategy objective. Each of the 100 homework activities is comprised of at least one photocopiable page to send home. Each sheet provides instructions for the child and a brief note to the helper (be that a parent, grandparent, neighbour or sibling), stating simply and clearly its purpose and suggesting support and/ or a further challenge to offer the child. Every sheet is clearly marked with a W (word), S (sentence) or T (text) symbol to designate its main focus. (Please note that 'they', 'them', 'their' has sometimes been used in the helper and teachers' notes to refer to 'child'. This avoids the 'he or she' construction.)

Making the most of these resources

The best way to use these homework resources is to use them flexibly, integrating them with a sequence of literacy sessions over a number of days. Such an approach will also ensure that the needs of an individual, or groups of children, are met in different ways. Some of the homework sheets will be greatly enhanced by enlarging them to A3 size as this provides children with more space in which to write. Others, for example, the sets of story cards, lend themselves to being laminated for reuse.

Here are some ideas for different types of use:

Preparation

● Give a word- or sentence-level homework activity to prepare for a skills session later in the week. This allows the skill to be reviewed in less time, thus leaving more time for group activities.
● Give a text-level homework activity as a way of preparing for more detailed work on a particular type of text in a future literacy lesson.
● Give work on a particular short text as preparation for further work on that text, or a related text, in a future lesson.

Follow-up

● Give a word- or sentence-level homework activity as a follow-up to a literacy lesson to provide more practice in a particular skill.
● Give a text-level homework activity as a creative way of responding to work done in a literacy lesson.
● Use one of the many short texts as a follow-up to a study of a similar type of text in a lesson.

Reinforcement

● Give selected word- or sentence-level homework to specific children who need extra practice.
● Give a text-level homework activity to specific children to reinforce text-level work done in class.
● Use a short text with specific children to reinforce work done on similar texts.

Supporting your helpers

The importance of involving parents in homework is generally acknowledged. For this reason, as well as the 'Dear Helper' note on each homework sheet, there is also a homework diary sheet on page 128 which can be photocopied and sent home with the homework. Multiple copies of these can be filed or stapled together to make a longer-term homework record. For each activity, there is space to record its title, the date on which it was sent home and spaces for responses to the work from the helper, the child and the teacher. The homework diary is intended to encourage home-school links, so that parents and carers know what is being taught and can make informed comments about their child's progress. It is also worth writing to parents and helpers, or holding a meeting, to discuss their role. This could include an explanation of how they can support their children's homework, for example, by:
● providing a space where the child can concentrate and has the necessary resources to hand;
● becoming actively involved by interpreting instructions, helping with problems, sharing reading and participating in the paired activities where required.

Discuss with them how much time you expect the child to spend on the homework. If, after that time, a child is stuck, or has not finished, then suggest to the parent/helper that they should not force the child to continue. Ask them to write an explanation and the teacher will give extra help the next day. However, if children are succeeding at the task and need more time, this can be allowed – but bear in mind that children need a varied and balanced home life!

It is worth discussing with parents what is meant by 'help' as they should be careful that they do not go as far as doing the homework for the child. Legitimate help will include sharing the reading of texts, helping to clarify problems, discussing possible answers, etc, but it is important that the child is at some stage left to do his or her best. The teacher can then form an accurate assessment of the child's strengths and weaknesses and provide suitable follow-up work.

Using the activities with the All New 100 Literacy Hours series

A cross-referenced grid has been provided (on pages 5, 6 and 7) for those who wish to use these homework activities with the corresponding All New 100 Literacy Hours book. The grid suggests if and where a homework task might fit within the context of the appropriate All New 100 Literacy Hours unit and there may be more than one appropriate activity. Sometimes, the homework page could be used for a skills session in class and one of the resources from All New 100 Literacy Hours can be used for homework.

PAGE	HOMEWORK TITLE	USE AS A FOLLOW ON TO:	NLS OBJECTIVE LINK	LINK TO 100 LITERACY HOURS
27	Look, cover, write, check (1)	Focusing on spelling	Y5 T1 W1	
28	More than one	Reading a text that contains y/ies plurals	Y5 T1 W5	
29	Irregular plurals	Reading a text that contains examples of irregular plurals	Y5 T1 W5	
30	Prefix it!	Investigating texts containing prefixes auto, bi, trans, tele, circum	Y5 T1 W6	Unit 6 Hour 2
31	Ship synonyms	Preparing for descriptive/poetic writing	Y5 T1 W7	Unit 3 Hour 4
32	Sleeping Beauty	Choosing the most effective synonym in context of story writing	Y5 T1 W7	Unit 1 Hour 5 Unit 3 Hour 7
33	Word clusters	Reading a text containing one or more listed word	Y5 T1 W8	
34	A sitting duck	Investigating idiomatic phrases in a text	Y5 T1 W9	Term 2 Unit 1 Hour 7
35	Adverb attack	Improving written dialogue	Y5 T1 W10	Unit 1 Hour 5 Unit 2 hour 3
36	Add an adverb	Improving descriptive writing	Y5 T1 W10	Unit 3 Hour 8
37	Editing	Redrafting a recently written story	Y5 T1 S3	Unit 1 Hour 5; Unit 3 Hour 10 Unit 5 Hour 5
38	Indirect dinosaurs	Looking at direct and reported speech in plays/ stories	Y5 T1 S5	Unit 2 Hour 1/2
39	Direct and reported	Looking at direct and reported speech in plays/ stories	Y5 T1 S5	Unit 2 Hour 2 Unit 1 Hour 2
40	Punctuation pointers	Reinforcing the purpose of punctuation	Y5 T1 S6	Unit 1 Hour 1 Unit 4 Hour 4
41	Old new school	Writing stories with dialogue to teach its conventions	Y5 T1 S7	Unit 1 Hour 2
42	Is it simple?	Looking at verb tenses; focusing on auxiliary verbs	Y5 T1 S8	Unit 5 Hour 1
43	Which person?	Considering viewpoint in a story; following up on personal pronouns	Y5 T1 S8	Unit 3 Hour 3 Unit 5 Hour 1
44	Video phone	Reading or writing instructions containing imperative verbs	Y5 T1 S9	Unit 6
45	Beginnings	Preparing to write a story beginning	Y5 T1 T1	Unit 1 Hour 2
46	Phrenological characters	Exploring characters in a story or novel	Y5 T1 T3	Unit 3 Hour 3
47	Mrs May	Exploring characters in a story or novel	Y5 T1 T3	Unit 3 Hour 3/6
48	Pleasant Sounds	Reading/writing poetry rooted in experience	Y5 T1 T4	Unit 4 Hour 3
49	Computer kids	Focusing on drama (conventions/improvising/ writing)	Y5 T1 T5	Unit 2
50	Meg Merrilies	Studying a range of poems, especially classic/serious	Y5 T1 T6	Unit 4 Hour 5
51	Poetry analyser	Investigating a range of poems; writing poems	Y5 T1 T7	Unit 4 Hour 5
52	Wild witches' ball	Exploring rhyme and alliteration in poems	Y5 T1 T7	Unit 4 Hour 1/5
53	Word play	Focusing on word play in poems/prose	Y5 T1 T8	Unit 4 Hour 2
54	The Gypsy Laddie	Extending an existing story in prose/poetry	Y5 T1 T15	Unit 1 Hour 5
55	The poetry processor	Writing poetry	Y5 T1 T16/17	Unit 4 Hour 3
56	Bedtime blues	Preparing to write playscripts. Links with page 49	Y5 T1 T18	Unit 2
57	The haunted house	Adding stage directions and performance notes to playscripts	Y5 T1 T19	Unit 2 Hour 1
58	Lusitania recount	Reading recounts	Y5 T1 T21	Unit 5 Hour 1/2
59	Failed Flying 10	Looking at key features of reports	Y5 T1 T26	
60	Newfoundland notes	Preparing for a lesson requiring research and note-making	Y5 T1 T26	Unit 5 Hour 3
61	Abbreviations	Practising note-making	Y5 T1 T27	Unit 5 Hour 3

PAGE	HOMEWORK TITLE	USE AS A FOLLOW ON TO:	NLS OBJECTIVE LINK	LINK TO 100 LITERACY HOURS
62	Look, cover, write, check (2)	Focusing on spelling	Y5 T2 W1	
63	Full to –ful	Reading texts that contain spelling pattern 'ful'	Y5 T2 W4	Unit 3 Hour 7
64	Dreadful language	Reading texts that contain common letter strings but different pronunciations	Y5 T2 W5	Unit 1 Hour 1
65	Homophone cards	Reading texts containing homophones	Y5 T2 W6	Unit 2 Hour 1
66	What do you do?	Looking at texts with words containing suffix 'cian'	Y5 T2 W8	Unit 3 Hour 1
67	Technical tangle	Investigating non-fiction texts containing technical words	Y5 T2 W9	Unit 1 Hour 10 Unit 5 Hour 2
68	Opposites attract	Investigating antonyms	Y5 T2 W10	Unit 2 Hour 3
69	Opposites by prefix	Investigating antonyms; potential links with page 68	Y5 T2 W10	
70	Onomatopoeia	Exploring poems containing onomatopoeia	Y5 T2 W11	Unit 2 Hour 4
71	Don't take it literally	Looking at figurative language in poems	Y5 T2 W12	
72	Table-top planet	Writing poems using figurative language	Y5 T2 W12	
73	Sickly soup	Turning simple sentences into complex ones	Y5 T2 S1	Unit 4 Hour 2
74	Are we agreed?	Consolidating understanding of concurrence between noun and verb	Y5 T2 S2	
75	Video audiences	Exploring technical terms in non-fiction writing; potential links with page 67	Y5 T2 S3	Unit 4 Hour 5
76	Proper or common?	Looking at parts of speech	Y5 T2 S4	
77	Trudy's Dream Present	Focusing on paragraphing and how sentences are linked through pronouns	Y5 T2 S4/10	Unit 2 Hour 2 Unit 3 Hour 4
78	Caribbean folk tale	Preparing to write a story	Y5 T2 S6/T3	Unit 1 Hour 3
79	Combine sentences	Looking at sentence building	Y5 T2 S8	Unit 4 Hour 2
80	Phantom phrases	Building sentences by embedding phrases and clauses	Y5 T2 S9	Unit 3 Hour 10
81	Mercury and the Forester	Investigating myths, legends, fables. Potential links with page 85/86	Y5 T2 T1	Unit 1 Hour 6/7/8
82	The Mistletoe Bough	Reading narrative poems	Y5 T2 T4	Unit 2 Hour 1
83	Overheard on a Saltmarsh	Focusing on features of oral poems e.g rhythm, rhyme, alliteration. Potential links with pages 114 and 122	Y5 T2 T5	Unit 2 Hour 5
84	All kinds of poems	Reading a range of poems	Y5 T2 T6	Unit 2 Hour 4
85	Arthur: chosen king	Exploring legends, myths and fables; potential links with pages 81 and 86	Y5 T2 T11	Unit 3 Hour 10
86	The Lambton worm	Exploring legends, myths and fables; potential links with pages 81 and 85	Y5 T2 T11	Unit 3
87	Write On	Writing extensions to poems/reading narrative poetry	Y5 T2 T12	Unit 2 Hour 3
88/89	Science fiction cards: plots and endings	Preparing to tell stories	Y5 T2 T14	Unit 3 Hour 5/10
90	Colour television	Looking at/preparing to write explanation texts	Y5 T2 T15	Unit 4 Hour 1
91	Concept mapping	Preparing for research	Y5 T2 T16	Unit 5 Hour 4
92	Scanning	Preparing for research by scanning texts	Y5 T2 T17	Unit 4 Hour 2 Unit 5 Hour 3
93	Internet download	Rewriting information located through research	Y5 T2 T20	Unit 5 Hour 3
94	Non-fiction redrafting checklist	Redrafting non-fiction writing	Y5 T2 T24	Unit 4 Hour 4/5 Unit 5 Hour 5

PAGE	HOMEWORK TITLE	USE AS A FOLLOW ON TO:	NLS OBJECTIVE LINK	LINK TO 100 LITERACY HOURS
95	Look, cover, write, check (3)	Focusing on spelling	Y5 T3 W1	
96	Achievement	Reading texts containing words with e+suffix	Y5 T3 W5	
97	Beautiful	Reading texts containing words with y+suffix	Y5 T3 W5	Unit 3 Hour 2
98	Except after c	Reading texts containing words with spelling rule i before e	Y5 T3 W5	
99	Verb to noun	Investigating how to change verbs to nouns	Y5 T3 W6	
100	Noun to verb	Investigating how to change nouns to verbs	Y5 T3 W6	
101	Adjective to adverb	Investigating how to change adjectives to adverbs	Y5 T3 W6	
102	From bad to worse	Reading texts that contain examples of comparative adjectives	Y5 T3 W6	
103	Linstead Market	Investigating dialect in texts	Y5 T3 W9	Unit 2 Hour 4
104	American English	Investigating dialect in texts	Y5 T3 W9	Unit 3 Hour 3
105	Hallucinate	Using dictionaries	Y5 T3 W11	Unit 3 Hour 1
106	Punctuation posers	Punctuating complex sentences; analysing sentence construction	Y5 T3 S4	
107	Punctuating Rapunzel	Punctuating complex sentences; analysing sentence construction	Y5 T3 S4	
108	Whose is it?	Revising use of apostrophe for possession	Y5 T3 S5	Unit 1 Hour 3
109	All in a good clause (1)	Investigating and analysing clauses by identifying the main clause. Potential links with pages 110; 111; 112	Y5 T3 S6	Unit 6 Hour 5
110	All in a good clause (2)	Investigating and analysing clauses. Potential links with pages 109; 111; 112	Y5 T3 S6	Unit 6 Hour 5
111	All in a good clause (3)	Investigating adverbial clauses. Potential links with pages 109; 110; 112	Y5 T3 S6	Unit 6 Hour 5
112	All in a good clause (4)	Investigating noun clauses. Potential links with pages 109; 110; 111	Y5 T3 S6	Unit 6 Hour 5
113	Join it	Using connectives to link clauses and sentences	Y5 T3 S7	Unit 4 hour 2 Unit 6 Hour 1
114	The Rain-Making Ceremony	Reading texts from a range of different cultures. Potential links with pages 83 and 122	Y5 T3 T1	Unit 1 Hour 1
115	Tramp trouble	Exploring character by describing events from another point of view	Y5 T3 T3	Unit 1 Hour 2
116	Anecdotes	Exploring character by describing events from another point of view. Potential links with page 78 or 115	Y5 T3 T3	Unit 1 Hour 2 Unit 3 Hour 4
117	The Mummers' play	Performing a play in verse	Y5 T3 T4	Unit 2 Hour 2
118	Phantom of Delight	Exploring older literature. Potential link with page 119	Y5 T3 T6	Unit 2 Hour 3 Unit 3 Hour 1/2
119	The Secret Garden	Exploring older/classic literature. Potential link with page 118	Y5 T3 T6/S6	Unit 3 Hour 1–3
120	Shakespeare's language	Looking at the differences in language between modern and older texts	Y5 T3 T6	
121	Desert island	Continuing to write a text in the style of the author	Y5 T3 T9	Unit 3 Hour 4
122	My Dad, Your Dad	Presenting performance poetry. Potential links with pages 83 and 114	Y5 T3 T11	Unit 2 Hour 5
123	Old school fields	Investigating examples of argument and persuasive writing. Potential links with pages 124–127	Y5 T3 T13	Unit 5 Hour 2
124	One kid crime wave	Investigating examples of argument and persuasive writing. Potential links with pages 123; 125–127	Y5 T3 T15	Unit 4 Hour 1
125	Book advertisement	Investigating examples of argument and persuasive writing. Potential links with pages 123–124; 126–127	Y5 T3 T15	Unit 4
126	Boreham supertram	Investigating examples of argument and persuasive writing. Potential links with pages 123–125; 127	Y5 T3 T17	Unit 5 Hour 3
127	Uniform arguments	Investigating examples of argument and persuasive writing. Potential links with pages 123–126	Y5 T3 T19	Unit 4 Hour 5 Unit 5 Hour 4

Teachers' notes

p27 LOOK, COVER, WRITE, CHECK (1)

Objective
Keep individual spelling lists of words and learn to spell them. (Y5, T1, W1)

Lesson context
Use with any lesson where spelling is a focus.

Setting the homework
Remind the children how to use the 'Look, Cover, Write, Check' method of learning spellings. Give them time to add their indiviudal spellings to the list.

Differentiation
The list is the first part of 100 commonly mis-spelled words for this age group. Words in the list should be adjusted for the most and least able. The most important way to differentiate is to ensure that the children add their own words.

Back at school
Reinforce learning by asking the children to test each other in pairs. Emphasise the fun rather than the test element.

p28 MORE THAN ONE

Objective
Investigate and learn spelling rules: y/ies plurals. (Y5, T1, W5)

Lesson context
Shared or guided reading of a text that provides several examples of y/ies plurals.

Setting the homework
Go over explanation. Encourage the children to use common sense. If they apply the rules wrongly, words will look wrong.

Differentiation
This is a simple rule which is a matter of practice. All the children should attempt the homework.

Back at school
The misapplication of this rule is one of the commonest causes for spelling mistakes; the children's writing, therefore, should be monitored to see how well they are applying the rule.

p29 IRREGULAR PLURALS

Objective
Investigate and learn spelling rules: irregular plurals. (Y5, T1, W5)

Lesson context
Shared or guided reading of a text which provides several examples of irregular plurals.

Setting the homework
Go over the explanation and examples. Emphasise the difference between English irregular plurals and those from Greek and Latin. The former are well known, the latter need to be carefully learned.

Differentiation
For less able children, delete words which they may not have encountered before, so that they can concentrate on the other, more commonly used, plurals.

Back at school
Monitor the use of irregular plurals in the children's writing.

p30 PREFIX IT!

Objective
Investigate the meanings and spellings of words using prefixes: auto, bi, trans, tele, circum. (Y5, T1, W6)

Lesson context
Use as a follow up to any text that provides examples of some of these prefixes.

Setting the homework
Revise the term prefix (letters added to the beginning of a word to change its meaning) and root (the basic part of a word), and explain how to play the game.

Differentiation
Write to parents of the less able, emphasising how important it is that they understand the meanings of these words.

Back at school
Ensure children know the meanings of words they made.

p31 SHIP SYNONYMS

Objective
Explain the differences between synonyms. (Y5, T1, W7)

Lesson context
This homework is good preparation for descriptive and poetic writing.

Setting the homework
Revise the meaning of the word synonym. Synonyms are words of similar meaning. No two words mean exactly the same, even if they are very similar, eg 'terrified' is stronger than 'frightened'. A good writer finds the synonym with exactly the meaning they want.

Differentiation
Most children would benefit from the support of dictionaries and thesauri. If possible, supply these to the children ensuring, of course, that they know how to use them.

Back at school
Encourage the creative use of synonyms in descriptive writing and poetry and ensure that a thesaurus is readily available for writing sessions.

p32 SLEEPING BEAUTY

Objective
Explain the differences between synonyms. (Y5, T1, W7)

Lesson context
Set this homework immediately before story writing as it provides a good model for choosing the most effective synonym in context.

Setting the homework
Explain to the children that they should avoid choosing words which are boring, eg 'nice', inappropriate, eg 'guy', or repetitive, eg 'prickly' in both the third and fourth sentences.

Differentiation
The more able children could be encouraged to find their own synonyms to fill the gaps.

Back at school
Discuss the synonyms chosen by the children and their reasons for choosing them.

p33 WORD CLUSTERS

Objective
Identify word roots, derivations and spelling patterns. (Y5, T1, W8)

Lesson context
Use as a follow-up to reading any text which contains one or more of the words listed.

Setting the homework
Talk about the example 'electric' and explain how the addition of different prefixes and suffixes have been used to make lots of related words.

Differentiation
Less able children could be asked to do the first three words only. More able children could be asked to tackle the extension activity.

Back at school
Share the word clusters. Who found the most words for each cluster? What other words were investigated?

p34 A SITTING DUCK

Objective
Collect and classify a range of idiomatic phrases. (Y5, T1, W9)

Lesson context
Use in the context of a language investigation into idiomatic phrases, clichés and expressions or when teaching a text in which several are used.

Setting the homework
Explain that common sayings and clichés are often used by adults, but can be mystifying to children and foreigners learning the language. Tell the children that if they do not know the meaning of a saying, they should ask an adult.

Differentiation
Children who do not start off with a knowledge of at least some of the sayings could be asked to find out about any five of them. If appropriate dictionaries are not available, the children should be encouraged to ask others for the meanings.

Back at school
Discuss what the sayings mean and talk about contexts in which they may be used.

p35 ADVERB ATTACK

Objective
Use adverbs to qualify verbs in writing dialogue. (Y5, T1, W10)

Lesson context
During or after a series of lessons on how to improve written dialogue. The series of lessons might adopt the following structure: use speech marks, use speech marks plus additional punctuation, set out speech with a new indented line for each change of speaker, use synonyms of 'said' in the reporting clause, add an adverb to the reporting clause.

Setting the homework
Revise the term adverb and use the example to show where the adverb is usually placed.

Differentiation
Children who have not mastered the earlier lessons in the series should work at the stage which is most appropriate to them.

Back at school
Apply this skill to the context of writing a story with dialogue as soon as possible after the homework.

p36 ADD AN ADVERB

Objective
Use adverbs to qualify verbs. (Y5, T1, W10)

Lesson context
This homework is most effective in a lesson or series of lessons which teach children how to improve description. Rather than a 'one off', this homework should be repeated with other verbs, so that the children build up a bank of verbs with suitable adverbs.

Setting the homework
Revise the terms verb and adverb. Explain that a well-chosen adverb can enhance the descriptive power of a piece of writing.

Differentiation
Children who do not understand the terms verb and adverb should be given reinforcement work on those terms and do this homework later.

Back at school
Share adverbs and ask the children to add any new ones they like to their list.

p37 EDITING

Objective
Discuss, proof-read and edit own writing. (Y5, T1, S3)

Lesson context
Give this homework as preparation for redrafting a recently-written story. It will show the children what to look for when redrafting so that they improve description and vocabulary as well as technical features.

Setting the homework
Explain that the notes are to there help. For example, if the note says 'punctuation', there is a punctuation mistake in the line opposite. After editing, the children should produce a neatly written, improved version.

Differentiation
Notes for the less able could be simplified, eg reference to grammatical errors could be dropped.

Back at school
Discuss the errors that the children found and their suggestions for improvement. The most important thing is to apply the skill to redrafting a piece of their own work.

p38 INDIRECT DINOSAURS

Objective
Understand the difference between direct and reported speech. (Y5, T1, S5)

Lesson context
Use with lessons on reading or writing stories or plays. Note that there is nothing difficult about direct and reported (or indirect) speech – children use it all the time. The more it is kept in a realistic context, the easier it will be.

Setting the homework
The main point of this homework is the simple recognition of reported speech. Tell children to look for the phrase 'says'/'said that'. Point out that reported speech is sometimes indicated by other verbs of speech, such as 'told', 'asked', 'shouted'. There is an example in the text.

Differentiation
All the children should be able to do this.

Back at school
Use an OHP to go over the examples of indirect speech.

p39 DIRECT AND REPORTED

Objective
Understand the difference between direct and reported speech. (Y5, T1, S5)

Lesson context
Use with lessons on writing stories or plays.

Setting the homework
Go over the explanation on the sheet.

Differentiation
This is a more academic study of direct and reported speech and involves applying rules to change from one to the other. Children should be able to do the activity on page 38, 'Indirect Dinosaurs' before they attempt this one. Also, any children who do not understand the terms *clause, tense, personal pronoun*, will not be able to understand the rules and should work on those terms instead.

Back at school
Go over the answers to the two sets of sentences orally, while the children mark their own.

p40 PUNCTUATION POINTERS

Objective
Understand the need for punctuation as an aid to the reader. (Y5, T1, S6)

Lesson context
This homework provides valuable reinforcement on punctuation, as it demonstrates that punctuation is not just an irritation dreamed up by teachers; it is actually very helpful in making texts clear and easy to read.

Setting the homework
Explain that, for the homework to work properly, the two passages must be read aloud.

Differentiation
Only children who have progressed to the appropriate stage should be asked to do the second part of the second task, eg start a new indented line for each change of speaker. Children who have difficulty with this should do page 41, 'Old New School'.

Back at school
Go over the correct punctuation using an OHP. Hopefully, a more positive climate will have been created for further work on punctuation!

p41 OLD NEW SCHOOL

Objective
Understand how dialogue is set out. (Y5, T1, S7)

Lesson context
Use when teaching the writing of stories with dialogue.

Setting the homework
It is worth pointing out examples of the setting out of speech in real stories. Also, page 40, 'Punctuation Pointers', should be done first, so that the children see how confusing it is when speech is not set out in this way.

Differentiation
Children must be confident about punctuating speech before they can tackle this step. Otherwise, there will be so much detail to remember they are likely to get confused. Children who are not ready for this step, should be given a sheet for a previous step, such as adding speech marks to dialogue.

Back at school
Apply the skill in writing stories with dialogue. There is a lot to remember when writing dialogue, so do not despair if it takes the children a while to remember it all.

p42 IS IT SIMPLE?

Objective
Investigate how different tenses are formed by using auxiliary verbs. (Y5, T1, S8)

Lesson context
In lessons on verb tenses, this would come towards the end with the more advanced work.

Setting the homework
Explain the terminology used and that the task is basically a sorting exercise.

Differentiation
Auxiliary verbs and the concept of 'simple' and 'continuous' tenses are quite advanced. This homework is for the more able children. Certainly, any children who do not understand the terms *verb* and *tense* should be given work on those concepts instead.

Back at school
Check the sorting exercise individually.

p43 WHICH PERSON?

Objective
Revise 1st, 2nd and 3rd person. (Y5, T1, S8)

Lesson context
Use in conjunction with a study of viewpoint in a story. Alternatively, use as the follow-up to a lesson on personal pronouns.

Setting the homework
Go over the explanation, particularly the conjugation of the verb, 'to be'. Note that the past tense has been chosen because this is the usual story telling tense. This will help the children to see that each person has both singular and plural forms.

Differentiation
Less able children should be able to do this exercise in a mechanical way, ie, by looking for the words 'I', 'you', though they may not fully grasp the concept of point of view. Do not worry about this because at least a start has been made.

Back at school
Identify the viewpoint of each text. When the children next write a story, encourage them to try a viewpoint they have not used very often.

p44 VIDEO PHONE

Objective
Identify the imperative form and read and write instructional writing. (Y5, T1, S9)

Lesson context
This homework goes well with a lesson on reading or writing instructions, or a grammar lesson on the imperative mood.

Setting the homework
Encourage the children to read the instructions carefully and then act out making a call. While doing this, an adult should check that they are carrying out the instructions correctly.

Differentiation
Explain to less able children that 'imperative' simply means 'something you must do'. Thus, if you do not follow one of the instructions, your call will not get through. Ask them to underline the words which say 'what you must do'.

Back at school
Share the instructions the children have written and use them to collect more examples of imperative verbs.

p45 BEGINNINGS

Objective
Analyse the features of a good opening and to compare a number of story beginnings. (Y5, T1, T1)

Lesson context
Ideal preparation for story writing as it encourages children to give thought to what makes a good beginning.

Setting the homework
Tell the children that the homework will be preparation for writing their own story, so it is important to think about what, in a story, makes you want to read on. They should also think about the kind of beginning they would like to use.

Differentiation
All children should be able to do this task.

Back at school
Discuss the different beginnings. Ask: *What type are they? What makes you want to read on? What do you think happens next?* Children should plan their stories soon after this homework.

p46 PHRENOLOGICAL CHARACTERS

Objective

Investigate how characters are presented. (Y5, T1, T3)

Lesson context
Use this as a follow-up to the study of a character or characters in a story or novel.

Setting the homework
Explain that phrenology was once thought to be a science. Phrenologists believed that they could read a person's character by reading the bumps on their heads. Ask the children to look at the diagram while you go over some of the more difficult terms, eg 'conscientious'.

Differentiation
This is a fun approach to the study of character, so all the children should attempt it. Less able children will need help with some of the terms. Definitions of the four or five most difficult words could be written on the back of their sheets.

Back at school
Discuss which bumps the children shaded in to describe the characters. If time allows, a fun follow-up would be to ask the children to try to read each others' characters.

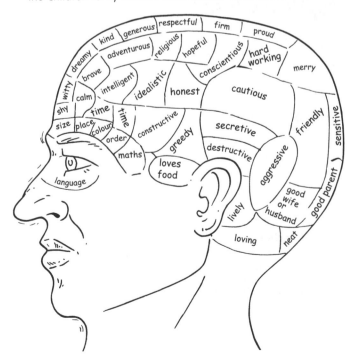

p47 MRS MAY

Objective
Investigate how characters are presented through dialogue, action and description. (Y5, T1, T3)

Lesson context
Preparation for study of a character or characters in a novel.

Setting the homework
Explain that authors help us to get to know their characters by what they say (dialogue), what they do (action) and how they describe them. By the end of the book, we almost feel we know the character like a real person. The homework is to look for these things in the description of Mrs May.

Differentiation
Less able children should concentrate on reading, underlining and talking about what Mrs May is like.

Back at school
Ask the children to compare what they highlighted and read their descriptions of Mrs May (or what they discussed with their helper). Build up a composite description of Mrs May by making notes.

p48 PLEASANT SOUNDS

Objective
Consider how texts can be rooted in the writer's experience. (Y5, T1, T4)

Lesson context
Use in a lesson or series of lessons on reading and writing poetry. The homework makes an effective counter-balance to a lesson which has focused on the technical aspects of poetry.

Setting the homework
Give the children some brief information about the poet. John Clare was born in 1793 at Helpston in Northamptonshire and died in 1864. He was an uneducated country boy, but wrote some of England's finest nature poetry. The things he describes in the poem were a part of his everyday life.

Differentiation
Less able children may need help reading the poem, especially Clare's poetic and dialect words, eg 'crumping' (sound ice makes when you tread on it) and 'puddock' (a game bird).

Back at school
Discuss the differences between the everyday lives of Clare and the children. These could be quite revealing and worthy of further discussion, eg which kind of life is happiest, best? Ask the children to take notes on their experiences and develop them into a poem. Clare's poem is a good model as the poetry is in the detailed observation and careful choice of words, rather than in technicalities of rhythm and rhyme.

p49 COMPUTER KIDS

Objective
Understand dramatic conventions. (Y5, T1, T5)

Lesson context
This homework would fit into the following sequence of lessons: improvised drama to explore and work out ideas, preparing the rough draft of a script, studying conventions of script writing (this homework), preparing script for performance.

Setting the homework
Explain that the purpose of the task is to focus on the different conventions of scriptwriting. Emphasise that they should first read and enjoy the play scene with their helper.

Differentiation
The problem for the less able might be in applying all the conventions to an actual script. Put them in small groups and make the scriptwriting a group task.

Back at school
Soon after the homework, the children should apply the conventions to their playscripts, keeping the highlighted homework page in front of them as a model.

p50 MEG MERRILIES

Objective
Read a number of poems by significant poets. (Y5, T1, T6)

Lesson context
The study of this poem should be part of a programme of studying poems of all kinds. It is a good introduction to the more serious work of Keats and other classic poets.

Setting the homework
Give the children some brief information about the poet. Despite his short life (1795 to 1821), Keats wrote some of the finest poems in the English language.

Differentiation
Less able children should read the poem with their helper and talk about it. Others should also write about it. If page 51, 'Poetry Analyser', was used, share some of the responses.

Back at school
The poem is a character description. Read the poem again and discuss what kind of person Meg Merrilies was.

p51 POETRY ANALYSER

Objective
Analyse poetic style. (Y5, T1, T7)

Lesson context
In a planned programme of reading and studying poems of all kinds, old and new, this can be used in shared writing sessions as a model of how to write about poems. The aim is that children will be able to write without the 'frame' (especially the more able children).

Setting the homework
The children should be given a poem to write about. The poem could be read and discussed. If possible, enlarge the sheet to A3 so that children have space in which to write.

Differentiation
The more able should use the headings as guides and write in paragraphs on a separate sheet of paper. Less able may need to leave out all or part of the section on form.

Back at school
Use the responses as a focus for a discussion of the poem.

p52 WILD WITCHES' BALL

Objective
Analyse poetic style: the impact of rhyme, internal rhyme and alliteration. (Y5, T1, T7)

Lesson context
In a programme of reading and studying poems, choose examples of specific poetic techniques. This poem is an excellent example of the use of rhyme, internal rhyme and alliteration.

Setting the homework
Revise the meaning of the terms. Also, some information on the poet might be of interest to the children. Jack Prelutsky was born in 1940 in Brooklyn, New York. He is famous for his scary and humorous poems for children.

Differentiation
Less able children could concentrate on finding rhyme and alliteration only. Alliteration might be a difficult word to remember and spell, but it is an easy concept to grasp!

Back at school
Use an OHP of the poem and, in discussion with the children, highlight all the examples of rhyme, internal rhyme and alliteration. Then, read and enjoy the poem again!

p53 WORD PLAY

Objective
Investigate examples of word play. (Y5, T1, T8)

Lesson context
Any lesson in which word play in prose or poetry has been the focus.

Setting the homework
Explain that the sheet contains four funny poems in which the poets have played with words to create the humour. Read one aloud before the children go home.

Differentiation
All the children will enjoy the humour of these poems, although not all will be able to articulate how the humour is achieved.

Back at school
As the homework involves reading and discussing, with no written outcome required, it is important to follow it up in the classroom. Ask the children to share their responses and perhaps, select a few to read the poems aloud.

p54 THE GIPSY LADDIE

Objective
Write new scenes into a story in the manner of the writer. (Y5, T1, T15)

Lesson context
Use as a follow-up to any lesson focusing on stories in prose or verse. Writing new scenes into a story is a creative way of exploring plot and character. A ballad tells a story in a short, compact way and provides plenty of opportunities for creative additions.

Setting the homework
If time allows, read the ballad and give examples for new scenes. For example, what does the girl do when she gets tired of poverty?

Differentiation
The more able children should be encouraged to add their scenes in the same verse form. Other children could write their scenes in prose.

Back at school
Share the new scenes which have been created. Use as many as possible to create the 'full' version of the story. Children could finish off by writing full versions in verse or prose, incorporating any of the ideas they liked.

p55 THE POETRY PROCESSOR

Objective
Convey feelings or reflections in a poem/write metaphors. (Y5, T1, T16,17)

Lesson context
This is an ideal follow up to a lesson on writing poetry. It is particularly useful for those children who found it hard to think about what to write.

Setting the homework
Explain how to use the cards. Emphasise that the 'Poetry Processor' works best if they respond quickly to the prompt.

Differentiation
Less able children may need help with some technical terms, eg *adjective*, *adverb*, *verb*, *simile*. Definitions could be written on a separate sheet. For the least able, cards containing these terms should be omitted.

Back at school
Give an opportunity for the children to share their poems. If time allows, develop them.

p56 BEDTIME BLUES

Objective
Write own playscript. (Y5, T1, T18)

Lesson context
This homework is good preparation for writing playscripts, as it converts raw dialogue into a playscript using the appropriate conventions. It is a good follow up to page 49, 'Computer kids'.

Setting the homework
Use page 49 to remind the children of the conventions used in playscripts. Ideally, the children should take that page home along with this page. Explain that many scripts contain notes explaining how to stage the scene most effectively, the purpose of the second part of the activity.

Differentiation
Less able children should concentrate on the first part.

Back at school
Ensure the children apply the skill to writing their playscripts.

p57 THE HAUNTED HOUSE

Objective
Annotate a section of a playscript for performance. (Y5, T1, T19)

Lesson context
Use as part of a series of lessons on writing playscripts. In such a series, this would come towards the end as it focuses on the final refinements – the stage directions and performance notes.

Setting the homework
Ensure that the children understand the task by giving examples. An example of a stage direction might be: (after line 1) 'Joanne grabs Tanya's hand and pulls her back'. An example of performance notes is: 'The scene is set outdoors at night. Two girls are approaching an old house. Spooky sounds can be heard.'

Differentiation
Less able children could write stage directions only. More able should write a page of performance notes.

Back at school
Discuss the stage directions and performance notes and try some of them out in the hall or drama studio. Apply stage directions and performance notes to scripts being developed in drama lessons.

p58 LUSITANIA RECOUNT

Objective
Identify the features of recounted texts. (Y5, T1, T21)

Lesson context
Use as a follow-up to shared and guided reading of recounts. The homework will reinforce knowledge of the key features of the recount genre.

Setting the homework
Go over the task, making sure that the children understand each term, eg *temporal connectives*.

Differentiation
More able children should do the task on the Captain's log book.

Back at school
Revise the features of recounted texts. Using an OHP, go through the homework text and ask the children to volunteer to mark it up using different coloured pens.

p59 FAILED FLYING 10

Objective
Write notes for a report. (Y5, T1, T26)

Lesson context
Use as a follow-up to work on reports. The homework will reinforce knowledge of the key features of the report genre.

Setting the homework
Go over the features of report genre and explain that this report is written in notes on a pre-printed format, so full sentences are not used. Explain that the second part of the task is best done by designing a blank format and then filling it in the same way. Children could ask their parents about their experiences of similar reports, eg the MOT test.

Differentiation
Less able children may need help with some vocabulary, eg 'underinflated'.

Back at school
Share and compare reports which the children have written.

p60 NEWFOUNDLAND NOTES

Objective
Make notes for different purposes. (Y5, T1, T26)

Lesson context
This homework is good preparation for a humanities lesson that involves research and note-making.

Setting the homework
Explain that the purpose of the table is to ensure that the children do not write full sentences when note-making. The table format is used to make children focus on key words and numbers only.

Differentiation
Less able children might find it easier if they highlighted key words and numbers before filling in the table.

Back at school
Apply the skill to a real research context.

p61 ABBREVIATIONS

Objective
Use simple abbreviations. (Y5, T1, T27)

Lesson context
This fits in well with dictionary work or work on note-making.

Setting the homework
Explain the purpose of abbreviations. Full stops are used to indicate abbreviations but commonly used abbreviations usually omit full stops (American English and older British English use full stops after Dr., Mr., etc.)

Differentiation
All the children should be able to do this homework.

Back at school
Monitor the children's use of abbreviations in context, ensuring that they are appropriate and correctly punctuated.

p62 LOOK, COVER, WRITE, CHECK (2)

Objective
Keep individual spelling lists of words and learn to spell them. (Y5, T2, W1)

Lesson context
Use with any lesson where spelling is a focus.

Setting the homework
Remind the children how to use the 'Look, Cover, Write, Check' method of learning spellings. Give the children time to add their individual spellings to the list.

Differentiation
The list is the second part of 100 commonly mis-spelled words for this age group. Words included should be adjusted for the most and least able. Ensure that they add their words to the list.

Back at school
Reinforce learning by asking the children to test each other.

p63 FULL TO -FUL

Objective
Explore spelling patterns: *ll* in *full* becomes *l* when used as a suffix. (Y5, T2, W4)

Lesson context
Follow-up to reading text that contains several examples.

Setting the homework
Revise the terms *noun* and *adjective*. Warn children to watch out for words ending in *y*.

Differentiation
All the children should be able to do this homework.

Back at school
Monitor the application of this rule in the children's writing.

p64 DREADFUL LANGUAGE

Objective
Investigate words which have common letter strings, but different pronunciations. (Y5, T2, W5)

Lesson context
Use as a follow-up to reading any text that contains examples of some of these letter strings.

Setting the homework
Use the explanation to discuss some of the difficulties in English spelling. Reassure the children that some words are awkward and tricky, but they just have to be learned.

Differentiation
This basic work on spelling will benefit all children.

Back at school
Share other examples of words with the same letter strings, as those in the poem.

p65 HOMOPHONE CARDS

Objective
Distinguish between homophones. (Y5, T2, W6)

Lesson context
Use with any text where homophones appear, or as a follow up to a spelling lesson.

Setting the homework
Explain that homophones, though they sometimes cause spelling problems, are helpful as they remind us of different meanings. For example, a television 'programme' is spelled differently to a computer 'program'. It is also worth pointing out that homophones are used to make up jokes (when they are called *puns*), eg 'Is a vicar's budgie a bird of pray?'

Differentiation
Less able children could be given sheets with the more difficult words deleted, eg 'principal'/'principle', 'profit'/'prophet'.

Back at school
Create an interactive homophone display using the cards. Encourage the children to add more homophones.

p66 WHAT DO YOU DO?

Objective
Recognise and spell the suffix -*cian*. (Y5, T2, W8)

Lesson context
Use with any text that contains words with this *suffix*, or as part of a series of lessons on spelling rules pertaining to suffixes.

Setting the homework
Go over the explanation on the sheet and explain what to write on the cards.

Differentiation
The less able might cut the pictures out to make cards which the helper can use as flash cards. The child can say the -*cian* words before writing them.

Back at school
Go over the pictures and check that all the children know how to form and spell the -*cian* words.

p67 TECHNICAL TANGLE

Objective
Search for, define and spell technical terms. (Y5, T2, W9)

Lesson context
Use this homework in a study of non-fiction texts, particularly texts of a technical nature such as computer manuals, scientific works.

Setting the homework
Explain that technical terms are often difficult, but necessary to allow precise description in specific areas of study. There are about 500 000 technical terms in the English language. Encourage the children to have fun with this activity. It is a sort of detective game in which they have to find and highlight the terms. The highlighted terms act as a guide to re-sequencing the text. Each child will need five different coloured highlighters or pens, as well as scissors and paste.

Differentiation
Technical terms are difficult. This exercise may be beyond some less able children. They could identify technical terms in a simpler text. Most school textbooks, especially science books should provide suitable passages.

Back at school
Ask for volunteers to read out the re-sequenced texts, then discuss the technical terms and what they mean. Ask the question: *Are there any places where ordinary words could have been used instead?*

p68 OPPOSITES ATTRACT

Objective
Investigate *antonyms*. (Y5, T2, W10)

Lesson context
Investigating antonyms is a way of extending vocabulary. This homewok can be used with any lessons in which vocabulary is a focus.

Setting the homework
Explain how to link up the opposites with a line by drawing attention to the example on the sheet.

Differentiation
The task is not difficult. Some words may prove difficult for less able children. Encourage them to do as many as they can and leave those they are not sure about.

Back at school
Discuss some of the opposites, eg 'employer', 'employee'.

p69 OPPOSITES BY PREFIX

Objective
Investigate antonyms. (Y5, T2, W10)

Lesson context
This is a useful follow-up to the previous work and other lessons on *prefixes*.

Setting the homework
It is important that the children understand that each word has a specific prefix. These will not work on a 'pick and mix' basis.

Differentiation
Many of the opposites are quite difficult words both in spelling and meaning. Less able children should do page 68, 'Opposites attract', instead.

Back at school
Write in the correct prefixes as the children suggest them.

p70 ONOMATOPOEIA

Objective
Explore onomatopoeia. (Y5, T2, W11)

Lesson context
Use as part of a programme of studying poetry. The children should be given poems with examples of onomatopoeia and should try it for themselves.

Setting the homework
Explain the term *onomatopoeia* by using the explanation.

Differentiation
All children will enjoy playing with the words and writing their own onomatopoeic poems.

Back at school
Share and enjoy the children's onomatopoeic poems.

p71 DON'T TAKE IT LITERALLY

Objective
Investigate metaphorical expressions and figures of speech. (Y5, T2, W12)

Lesson context
It is important that the children are introduced to figurative language early in their study of poetry. There are about ten commonly used figures of speech (*allegory, allusion, hyperbole, irony, litotes, metaphor, metonomy, personification, simile, synecdoche*).

Setting the homework
Explain the difference between 'literal' and 'figurative'.

Differentiation
Children who cannot recognise and understand similes should do more work on them before going to this stage. Alternatively, they could do page 72, 'Table-top planet', which is easier.

Back at school
Share and discuss children's examples of literal and figurative language.

p72 TABLE-TOP PLANET

Objective
Investigate metaphorical expressions and figures of speech. (Y5, T2, W12)

Lesson context
This focuses on the application of figurative language to create imaginative poetry and is ideal for poetry writing.

Setting the homework
Make sure that the children understand the terms *literal* (realistic, factual) and *figurative* (imaginative, symbolic). Read the example to the children and discuss how the author has taken a simple object and looked at it in an imaginative way.

Differentiation
All the children should be able to do this sheet.

Back at school
Share examples of the literal–figurative poems.

p73 SICKLY SOUP

Objective
Re-order simple sentences; combine simple sentences. (Y5, T2, S1)

Lesson context
One important strand which runs through the Literacy Strategy is how to take simple sentences and build them into complex ones. This sheet can be used as a follow-up to that strand. It is also a good preparation for extended writing, whether fiction or non-fiction.

Setting the homework
Go over the examples, placing particular emphasis on the effect of re-ordering the sentences.

Differentiation
Most children should be able to do this sheet successfully, providing they understand the explanation. Those who cannot, probably need more work on writing correct simple sentences.

Back at school
Ask the children to share their re-ordered sentences. Ask the class to comment on the effect of each one: Ask: *Does the sentence make sense? What is the emphasis of the sentence? Have pronouns been used or changed appropriately?*

p74 ARE WE AGREED?

Objective
Consolidate agreement between noun and verb. (Y5, T2, S2)

Lesson context
Use this sheet as a follow-up to a writing task in which several mistakes of this kind have been found.

Setting the homework
Go over the explanation, placing particular emphasis on the tip at the end. Most people make mistakes about the agreement of noun and verb because the noun is expressed in such a way that it sounds plural.

Differentiation
In order to benefit from this sheet, the children need to understand the terms: 'noun', 'verb', 'singular' and 'plural'. Children who have not mastered any of these should be given appropriate consolidation work.

Back at school
Go through the sheet with the children who did the homework. Monitor future work for problems of agreement.

p75 VIDEO AUDIENCES

Objective
Understand how writing can be adapted for different audiences. (Y5, T2, S3)

Lesson context
This homework would be a good follow-up to page 67, 'Technical tangle', as it explores technical terms in context. It provides practice in re-wording a text and is a good preparation for 'writing in your own words' when researching in the library or on the Internet.

Setting the homework
Explain the task with particular attention to the three points of advice. Emphasise that the end-product must be a simple, readable text.

Differentiation
Less able children could write a simple description for young children of how to play a video cassette. You could highlight relevant vocabulary on the sheet to help them with spelling.

Back at school
Read out some of the texts and discuss the problems of simplifying a technical text.

p76 PROPER OR COMMON?

Objective
Revise different kinds of noun. (Y5, T2, S4)

Lesson context
This homework should be used as part of a sequence of lessons (or parts of lessons) which focus on parts of speech.

Setting the homework
Explore the explanation with the children. For example, what happens if one tries to make some proper nouns, plural, eg Humber Bridges. Is that correct? No, there is only one Humber Bridge.

Differentiation
As this is revision work, most children should find it within their capabilities. Remind the less able to look for the capital letters which begin proper nouns.

Back at school
Briefly go over the sorted lists, but spend more time on thinking of more examples for each category.

p77 TRUDY'S DREAM PRESENT

Objective
Revise the function of pronouns. (Y5, T2, S4, 10)

Lesson context
This homework could form part of a sequence of lessons on paragraph cohesion. It encourages the children to look at the way sentences are related and thus avoid unnecessary repetition of nouns or overuse of pronouns.

Setting the homework
Write this short paragraph on the board: 'Trudy is a pupil at St Mark's Primary School. Trudy is ten. Trudy has lots of friends'. Explain that these three sentences are correct, but don't 'hang together' to form a paragraph. Change Trudy in the second two sentences to 'she', and explain how the 'she' refers back to the proper noun 'Trudy' and makes the three sentences into one paragraph. Explain that 'she' is a pronoun. Revise the definition of pronoun and give examples.

Differentiation
Even children who get confused over the terms *noun* and *pronoun* can do the written task.

Back at school
Read examples of the task and discuss which has the best balance of repeated nouns and personal pronouns.

p78 CARIBBEAN FOLK TALE

Objective
Be aware of and explore the differences between spoken and written language. (Y5, T2, S6/T3)

Lesson context
This homework is a preparation for story writing. Throughout the year, children should be given different kinds of stimuli for story writing, of which stimuli from oral tradition will be one.

Setting the homework
Explain to the children that they must never think that spoken language is inferior to written language because it contains hesitations and repetitions. In the history of mankind, spoken language came first and in our personal histories and lives, spoken language comes first. Use the explanation to explain the differences between spoken and written language.

Differentiation
Less able children could omit the written task.

Back at school
Highlight examples of the differences between spoken and written language as the children feed them back. Hold an oral story-telling session in which the children relate their stories and anecdotes.

p79 COMBINE SENTENCES

Objective
Combine two or more sentences. (Y5, T2, S8)

Lesson context
Use as part of a series of lessons on sentence building. This focuses on combining sentences or clauses with a central conjunction.

Setting the homework
Revise the term *conjunction* – a conjunction is a joining word.

Differentiation
All the children should be able to do this homework even if they do not understand the term *conjunction*.

Back at school
Discuss the conjunctions the children used – in many cases, a number of equally correct answers are possible.

p80 PHANTOM PHRASES

Objective
Secure the use of the comma in embedding phrases and clauses within sentences. (Y5, T2, S9)

Lesson context
Use as part of a series of lessons on sentence building. This focuses on the phrase in apposition and how to punctuate it. It could also be used as preparation for story writing, or as part of the redrafting process. The emphasis then would be on how to enhance description by adding phrases in apposition.

Setting the homework
Explain that a phrase in apposition is extra description added to a sentence between two commas.

Differentiation
The is essentially a cloze exercise with all the possible answers listed above. It might be better to ask the least able to do half of the passage.

Back at school
Discuss which phrases fit which gaps. Encourage the children to use phrases in apposition to enhance descriptions.

p81 MERCURY AND THE FORESTER

Objective
Identify and classify the features of fables. (Y5, T2, T1)

Lesson context
This could be part of a series of lessons investigating myths, legends and fables. It could be linked with homework page 85, 'Arthur: chosen king' and page 86, 'The Lambton worm', both of which retell ancient legends.

Setting the homework
Explain the differences between myths, legends and fables. A myth explains important things about existence, eg Pandora's Box explains how suffering came into the world; a legend is a story based on events in the past which may or may not be true, eg King Arthur; a fable is a short story written to prove a moral.

Differentiation
Less able children will have difficulty in explaining how the fable is different from an ordinary story. Encourage them to look for obvious things, eg shorter, less dialogue, leads to a moral.

Back at school
Discuss how the fable is different from an ordinary story. Share examples of the fables leading to the same moral. Read more of Aesop's fables. Make a list of morals and ask children to choose one and write a fable to go with it.

p82 THE MISTLETOE BOUGH

Objective
Read a range of narrative poems. (Y5, T2, T4)

Lesson context
This is a well-written poem with a fascinating story and worthy of extended study. This homework could be given as preparation for more detailed work on the poem.

Setting the homework
Explain that the best way to bring out the excitement of the story is to read the poem with the rhythm of natural speech, pausing at punctuation NOT at the end of lines. Explain to the children that they have to read the poem and retell the story to their parent helper.

Differentiation
Less able children will require help to ensure full understanding of the story in the poem.

Back at school
Talk about the story in the poem and discuss similar incidents today, eg children who get caught in abandoned fridges. Further work could include one or more of the following: dramatise the poem, write a prose version or a modern version, study the rhyme and rhythm patterns; study the language.

p83 OVERHEARD ON A SALTMARSH

Objective
Perform poems in a variety of ways. (Y5, T2, T5)

Lesson context
Part of a series of lessons on the oral aspects of poetry, eg rhythm, rhyme, alliteration, reading aloud, performance.

Setting the homework
Poetry began thousands of years ago as an oral performance and this is still an important aspect of poetry. This poem by Harold Munro was written to be performed and the homework requires children to read the poem with their helper and plan a performance.

Back at school
Discuss ideas for performance of the poem. This could include simple movements, eg crouching to suggest a goblin. Discuss how the situation could be developed through improvisation. Give the children five minutes to discuss ideas in pairs, then ask for volunteers to perform the poem and improvise a continuation.

p84 ALL KINDS OF POEMS

Objective
Understand terms that describe different kinds of poem. (Y5, T2, T6)

Lesson context
Use as part of a sequence of lessons on poetry and give after children have read a range of poems. It could be complemented by a homework sheet which covered other kinds of poem, eg couplets, blank verse, rhyme royal, free verse.

Setting the homework
Explain that the task is to match the poems to the definitions. Emphasise how important it is to read and enjoy the poems first!

Differentiation
Spend a few minutes with the less able revising the terms: syllable, rhyme and rhythm.

Back at school
Check that the children have correctly matched the names of the forms to the poems. Read each poem and discuss how the form chosen for each one is suited to its subject matter – the bouncy rhythm of the limerick emphasises humour; the brevity of the haiku emphasises its focused thought; the long lines of the sonnet are appropriate to the solemnity of the subject; the two couplets of the clerihew are appropriate to its simplicity; the rhythm and rhyme of ballad form help the story to flow.

p85 ARTHUR: CHOSEN KING

Objective
Write a version of legends, myths and fables. (Y5, T2, T11)

Lesson context
This could be part of a series of lessons on legends, myths and fables (see also page 81,'Mercury and the Forester' and page 86, 'The Lambton worm').

Setting the homework
Brainstorm with the children what they know about the legend of King Arthur. Even today's generation can reconstruct the bare bones of the story. The discussion will serve to show the many different versions of the story. Encourage them to retell the story in any way they like.

Differentiation
Less able children may need help with some of the words in the text, eg *engraved, Candelmas, Pentecost, tournament, scabbard*.

Back at school
Share the different retellings of the legend.

p86 THE LAMBTOM WORM

Objective
Write a version of legends, myths and fables. (Y5, T2, T11)

Lesson context
This could be part of a series of lessons on legends, myths and fables (see also pages 81 and 85).

Setting the homework
Explain this is a simple version of 'choice' stories found in books like the 'Fighting Fantasy' series and in computer adventure games. Explain how to read the 'choice' story.

Back at school
Children should use the format to write their 'choice' stories based on myths or legends. Writing in this format reinforces a number of key skills: a) planning with a beginning, main character, series of events and a well-defined ending are essential or the choices will not work; b) it gives children experience of writing stories in the present tense; c) they can write their story in the second or third person.

p87 WRITE ON

Objective
Use the structure of poems to write extensions. (Y5, T2, T12)

Lesson context
In lessons on poetry, use a wide range of responses and writing. This could be used to develop the skill of writing extensions to poems, or as a study of classic narrative poetry.

Setting the homework
Read the beginning of the poem and discuss what the story is about. Point out that some of the unfamiliar vocabulary is glossed (use the term; they'll know the term *glossary*!).

Differentiation
Less able children could focus more on the story of the poem and write their extensions in prose.

Back at school
Share the children's responses to 'what happens next?' Ask for both prose and verse responses. Tell them that the poem goes on to tell how the abbot travels far and wide to find the answers, but returns unsuccessful. He meets a poor shepherd who, though lacking in education, has wit. He dresses up as the abbot and goes to the king, answering the questions in a witty manner. The king is impressed, rewards the shepherd and pardons the abbot.

p88/89 SCIENCE FICTION CARDS: PLOTS AND ENDINGS

Objectives
Prepare for oral story telling. (Y5, T2, T14)

Lesson context
Each set of cards can be used on its own or the two pages can be used together. Alternatively they can be used as extensions to the set of Science Fiction Cards in *100 Literacy Hours* for Year 5. Children choose cards from one or more categories at random to provide a stimulus for oral story telling.

Setting the homework
Demonstrate how to use the cards by choosing one (or more) cards at random and improvising a story.

Back at school
Invite volunteers to tell their oral stories to the class. Discuss the stories, using them as a basis to make points about story structure, character, description and so on. Then ask the children to produce written versions of their stories.

p90 COLOUR TELEVISION

Objective
Read a range of explanatory texts. (Y5, T2, T15)

Lesson context
Use in a study of explanation genre, or as preparation for reading or writing explanatory texts in other areas.

Setting the homework
Go over the main features of explanatory texts.

Differentiation
Children who do not understand any of the terms, eg *impersonal style, complex sentences* and *passive voice*, should look for and highlight examples of features they do understand.

Back at school
Highlight examples of the features of explanatory texts.

p91 CONCEPT MAPPING

Objective
Prepare for research by identifying what they already know and what they need to find out. (Y5, T2, T16)

Lesson context
This is an ideal preparation for research. It could be done as practice, then the process applied to a real research task.

Setting the homework
Re-draw the concept map, showing how it grows from thought processes.

Differentiation
Ensure that the less able children draw a concept map on a subject which they already know something about.

Back at school
Share examples of concept maps and discuss how the process helped to clarify what needs to be researched. After the process has been used to focus real research, ask the children to draw another concept map, showing more detail and fewer questions.

p92 SCANNING

Objective
Locate information through scanning. (Y5, T2, T17)

Lesson context
Scanning is a very important research skill so this is good preparation for a real research task, especially one which is primarily text-based.

Setting the homework
Explain that the first step is to know for what kind of information you are scanning. Next, run quickly through the text – more quickly than normal reading – scanning for key words (eg *bullies, victims, researchers*). When a key word is found, slow down and read around it. Explain it is important to time yourself and work as quickly as possible.

Differentiation
Less able children may take longer to find the information.

Back at school
Briefly discuss the task and the time taken, then move on quickly to applying the skill in a real research context.

p93 INTERNET DOWNLOAD

Objective
Note-making: discuss what is meant by 'in your own words'. (Y5, T2, T20)

Lesson context
Use in the later stages of the research process when the children have located the information they want and are preparing to write about it. IT-based information sources make it easy to download and print off text, so these skills are important.

Setting the homework
The task is broken down into stages. Go over them and apply each to the first sentence as exemplified in the sample beginning on the page.

Differentiation
The nature of this task is to take a text with a high level of language difficulty and make it simpler, thus the less able will find the original text a barrier. They should, therefore, be given a simpler note-making task such as page 60.

Back at school
Apply these skills to a real research task. When you suspect the children of copying something, encourage them to rewrite it.

p94 NON-FICTION CHECKLIST

Objective
Evaluate their work. (Y5, T2, T24)

Lesson context
This checklist is designed to be used in the final stages of writing non-fiction as a way of helping children with the re-drafting process. The checklist should help them re-draft future work.

Setting the homework
Run through the checklist, revising the terminology. Discuss the requirements of the particular genre.

Differentiation
Prepare specific checklists for the more and less able. Checklists for the more able could give more details about the requirements of each genre and be more demanding in the grammar and punctuation section. Checklists for the less able could be simpler, focusing on essential requirements.

Back at school
Complete the process by asking the children to start work on the final copies of their non-fiction texts.

p95 LOOK, COVER, WRITE, CHECK (3)

Objective
Keep individual spelling lists of words and learn to spell them. (Y5, T3, W1)

Lesson context
Use with any lesson where spelling is a focus.

Setting the homework
Remind the children how to use the 'Look, Cover, Write, Check' method of learning spellings. Give the children time to add their spellings. Additional blank pages in the same format could be added for children's words.

Differentiation
The list is the third part of 100 commonly mis-spelled words for this age group. Words included should be adjusted for the most and least able. However, the most important way to differentiate is to ensure that children add their own words.

Back at school
Reinforce learning by asking the children to test each other in pairs. Emphasise the fun rather than the test element.

p96 ACHIEVEMENT

Objective
Investigate and learn spelling rules: e + suffix. (Y5, T3, W5)

Lesson context
Use as a follow up to a lesson or part of a lesson on spelling or with any text that contains several examples.

Setting the homework
Go over the explanation and the first example in the table.

Differentiation
This is a basic spelling rule which all children should learn. If necessary, provide appropriate catch-up work.

Back at school
Use an OHP to write in the correct spellings in column three as children read them out – or ask the children to write them in. Monitor the application of this rule in the children's writing.

p97 BEAUTIFUL

Objective
Investigate and learn spelling rules: y + suffix. (Y5, T3, W5)

Lesson context
Use as a follow-up to a lesson or part of a lesson on spelling or with any text that contains several examples.

Setting the homework
Go over the explanation and the first example in the table.

Differentiation
This is a basic spelling rule which all children should learn. If necessary, provide appropriate catch-up work.

Back at school
Use an OHP to write in the correct spellings in column three as children read them out – or ask the children to write them in. Monitor the application of this rule in children's writing.

p98 EXCEPT AFTER C

Objective
Investigate and learn spelling rules: i before e. (Y5, T3, W5)

Lesson context
As a follow-up to a lesson or part of a lesson on spelling, or with any text that contains several examples.

Setting the homework
Go over the explanation.

Differentiation
This is a basic spelling rule which all children should learn.

Back at school
Use an OHP to write in the correct spellings in the gaps. Monitor the application of this rule in the children's writing.

p99 VERB TO NOUN

Objective
Transform words: changing verbs to nouns. (Y5, T3, W6)

Lesson context
Use as a follow-up to a lesson or part of a lesson on this aspect of spelling or with any text that contains examples.

Setting the homework
Go over the explanation and example on the sheet.

Differentiation
Encourage the more able to use some of the pairs of words in sentences.

Back at school
Ask selected children to share sentences.

p100 NOUN TO VERB

Objective
Transform words: changing nouns to verbs. (Y5, T3, W6)

Lesson context
Use as a follow up to a lesson on this aspect of spelling.

Setting the homework
Go over the explanation and example.

Differentiation
Encourage the more able to use some of the pairs of words in sentences.

Back at school
Ask selected children who made sentences to share them.

p101 ADJECTIVE TO ADVERB

Objective
Transform words: changing adjectives to adverbs. (Y5, T3, W6)

Lesson context
Use as a follow-up to a lesson or part of a lesson on this aspect of spelling or with any text that contains several examples.

Setting the homework
Go over the explanation and example.

Differentiation
You may wish to limit the number of words for the less able children. Encourage the more able to use some of the pairs of words in sentences to show they understand the different uses of adjectives and adverbs.

Back at school
Use the activity on an OHP to write in the correct adverbs. Ask selected children, who made up sentences with the words, to share them.

p102 FROM BAD TO WORSE

Objective
Transform words: comparison of adjectives. (Y5, T3, W6)

Lesson context
Use as a follow-up to a lesson or part of a lesson on this aspect of spelling, or with any text that contains examples.

Setting the homework
Go over the explanation and examples.

Differentiation
This activity should be within the capability of most children. The more able children should be encouraged to use the comparative forms in sentences.

Back at school
Use the activity on an OHP to write in the correct comparative forms. Ask selected children, who made up sentences with the words, to share them.

p103 LINSTEAD MARKET

Objective
Understand how words vary across dialects. (Y5, T3, W9)

Lesson context
Use following a shared or guided reading of a text that contains dialect or following a specific skills session on this aspect of language.

Setting the homework
Explain that they will be reading a traditional Caribbean poem, written in the local dialect. Go over the terms 'accent' and 'dialect' as explained on the sheet. Encourage them to read the poem through once, before re-reading it to do the activity.

Differentiation
Even if the children cannot figure out what some of the dialect words mean, they should be able to distinguish them from words that are just pronounced differently.

Back at school
Discuss differences of accent and dialect in the poem. *Accent*: me (my), wut (would), Lard (Lord), wat (what), Satiday (Saturday), an (and), marnin' (morning), brukfas' (breakfast), gran' (grand), de (the), linga (linger), mumma (mothers), fa weh (far away). *Dialect*: ackee (fruit), go a (to), quatty (thing), not a bite (not one customer bought anything), come (comes), feel/squeeze up (feels/squeezes the fruit), mek me (I have to), dem 'tan (those tangerines), buy yu (do you want to buy?), nyam (taste), pickney (children), no bring (won't take).

p104 AMERICAN ENGLISH

Objective
Understand how words vary across dialects. (Y5, T3, W9)

Lesson context
Use following a shared or guided reading of a text that contains dialect or following a specific skills session on this aspect of language.

Setting the homework
Explain to the children that they have to supply either the American word where the English is given, or the English equivalent when the American is given. Encourage them to ask others if they don't know.

Differentiation
All children, particularly if they are working with a helper, should be able to undertake this activity.

Back at school
Create a whole-class Anglo-American dictionary and encourage the children to add new words.

p105 HALLUCINATE

Objective
Use dictionaries and understand their purposes.
(Y5, T3, W11)

Lesson context
This should follow up specific skills work on the features and uses of dictionaries.

Setting the homework
This homework requires a dictionary. To ensure that no child is disadvantaged because they do not have one at home, give each child a dictionary along with the homework page.

Differentiation
You may wish to adapt the questions for some children, perhaps by limiting their search to only one or two dictionary features (eg meaning and part of speech).

Back at school
Discuss the children's answers to the questions. Ask: *Did all the dictionaries give the same information?* If not, discuss the importance of choosing suitable dictionaries for the task.

p106 PUNCTUATION POSERS

Objective
Use punctuation marks accurately in complex sentences.
(Y5, T3, S4)

Lesson context
This could be used to follow up specific skills work on punctuating complex sentences or following text-level work analysing an author's style and sentence construction.

Setting the homework
Remind the children that a complex sentence includes a main clause (that makes sense on its own) and a subordinate clause (that gives more information about the main clause).

Differentiation
Children who are not yet secure about complex sentences should be given more basic work identifying the components of complex sentences.

Back at school
Using a whiteboard or flipchart, ask selected children to write one sentence each as they have done in their homework, while the others check their own work. Discuss any problems that arise. Encourage and monitor the children's use of complex sentences in their writing.

p107 PUNCTUATING RAPUNZEL

Objective
Use punctuation marks accurately in complex sentences.
(Y5, T3, S4)

Lesson context
This could be used to follow up specific skills work on punctuating complex sentences or following text-level work analysing an author's style and sentence construction.

Setting the homework
Ensure that, even if the term 'phrase in apposition' is not secure, the children grasp the idea of 'extra information'.

Differentiation
Children who are not yet secure about complex sentences should be given more basic work.

Back at school
Using a whiteboard or flipchart, ask selected children to write one sentence each as they have done in their homework, while the others check their own work. Discuss any problems that arise. Monitor children's use of complex sentences in their writing.

p108 WHOSE IS IT?

Objective
Revise use of apostrophe for possession. (Y5, T3, S5)

Lesson context
Any lesson that focuses on the uses of the apostrophe, or following the reading of a text that has examples of the possessive apostrophe.

Setting the homework
Go through the explanation and the examples.

Differentiation
Less able should concentrate on one or two of the rules.

Back at school
Check the children's work either individually or as a group. Encourage the children to look at their use of the apostrophe.

p109 ALL IN A GOOD CLAUSE (1)

Objective
Investigate clauses through identifying the main clause.
(Y5, T3, S6)

Lesson context
The clause structure of sentences is best taught as part of a structured series of lessons. This, and the next three pages, form a 'mini' series on clause analysis. Note that the emphasis is on the word 'mini'. Clause analysis is a difficult skill which can only be treated fully at advanced level. The aim is to give children an idea of the basic principles.

Setting the homework
Revise the necessary key terms, eg *sentence, complex sentence, main clause, subordinate clause, subject, verb.* Go over the explanation. Though the terminology is difficult, the task is quite easy. So, even if the terminology doesn't come easily, the children will develop an implicit knowledge of the concept. If the correct terminology is used, it will eventually become part of the children's critical vocabulary.

Differentiation
Even at this level, clause analysis is difficult and abstract. It is not suitable for children who have not grasped basics, such as knowledge of parts of speech. Less able children could be given simpler, related work, such as joining clauses with conjunctions in a simple pre-set pattern (see page 79, 'Combine sentences' or page 113, 'Join it'.)

Back at school
Go over the exercise and consolidate with similar work.

p110 ALL IN A GOOD CLAUSE (2)

Objective
Investigate clauses through understanding how they are connected: adjective clauses. (Y5, T3, S6)

Lesson context
Use as part of a series in clause analysis or as a valuable way of helping children to enhance their descriptions.

Setting the homework
Revise necessary terminology, eg *adjective, clause*, and introduce the term *relative pronoun*. Relative pronouns, like conjunctions, join clauses together.

Differentiation
Though less able children may well be mystified by the terminology, they should have no difficulty filling the gaps by using their innate sense of 'what sounds right'.

Back at school
Go over the gap-filling exercise. Note that '*which*' and '*that*' are often interchangeable. Give further practice on expanding sentences with adjective clauses.

p111 ALL IN A GOOD CLAUSE (3)

Objective
Investigate clauses through understanding how they are connected: adverb clauses. (Y5, T3, S6)

Lesson context
Use as part of a series in clause analysis or as a valuable way of helping children to enhance their descriptions.

Setting the homework
Revise necessary terminology, eg *adverb, clause, subordinate clause, conjunction*. Add that there are two types of conjunctions: a) co-ordinating, which join clauses with equal weight. The commonest co-ordinating conjunctions are 'and' and 'but'; b) subordinating, which join a clause of lesser importance to the main clause. Subordinating conjunctions are listed.

Differentiation
Less able children should be encouraged to use common sense in choosing suitable conjunctions.

Back at school
Go over the exercise and encourage children to use subordinating conjunctions to create interesting sentences.

p112 ALL IN A GOOD CLAUSE (4)

Objective
Investigate clauses through understanding how they are connected: noun clauses. (Y5, T3, S6)

Lesson context
This should be used as part of a series in clause analysis. It is also a valuable way of helping children to enhance their descriptions.

Setting the homework
Revise necessary terminology, eg *noun, clause and relative pronoun* (additional relative pronouns are introduced on this page). Go over the explanation and example.

Differentiation
Less able children should have no difficulty filling in the gaps by using their common sense to choose suitable relative pronouns from the list.

Back at school
Go over the gap-filling exercise. Review the whole series on clause analysis and encourage children to use what they have learned to build up interesting sentences in different ways.

p113 JOIN IT

Objective
Use connectives to link clauses within sentences and sentences in longer texts. (Y5, T3, S7)

Lesson context
Use as a supplement to the series of homework activities in clause analysis (pages 109–112). The focus is on the use of central conjunctions both co-ordinating and subordinating.

Setting the homework
Revise the term *conjunction*: conjunctions are joining words. There are two types of conjunction: a) co-ordinating, which join clauses with equal weight; b) subordinating, which join a clause of lesser importance to the main clause. Ask children to look at the list of conjunctions on the sheet. Ask: *Can they remember which conjunctions are co-ordinating conjunctions and which are subordinating conjunctions?*

Differentiation
The level of difficulty of this sheet is below that of page 111, so it could be used as an alternative for the less able. For other children, it will provide valuable reinforcement.

Back at school
Discuss which conjunctions work best in each sentence.

p114 THE RAIN-MAKING CEREMONY

Objective
Investigate a range of texts from different cultures. (Y5, T3, T1)

Lesson context
This is one of a range of texts from different cultures that could be studied as a series of lessons.

Setting the homework
Explain that this text is from the oral tradition of the Lango people and thus has not been influenced by Western European literary culture. Children should read this aloud with their helper and discuss the importance of rain to the Lango people.

Back at school
Ask for some volunteers to perform the ceremony. Discuss the importance of rain to the Lango people. If time allows, find out more about the Lango people and the climate of Uganda.

p115 TRAMP TROUBLE

Objective
Describe a situation from the point of view of another character. (Y5, T3, T3)

Lesson context
Describing a situation from the point of view of another character is an excellent way to explore characters and situations in a novel. This could be set as a preparatory exercise before doing the same thing in class with a character or scene from a novel that is being studied.

Setting the homework
Explain the task. If time allows, read the passage and discuss how the viewpoint could be changed. Draw children's attention to the guidance notes after the passage.

Differentiation
Less able children may be helped by being given a starter, eg Tim and Tom (or girls' names if preferred) tried the iron ring on the church door. It turned and the door opened. Tom giggled, but Tim said, 'Shh...what's that breathing sound?'

Back at school
Share and discuss the rewritten stories. Apply the skill to a story that is currently being studied.

p116 ANECDOTES

Objective
Describe a situation from the point of view of another character. (Y5, T3, T3)

Lesson context
This page can provide further work following page 78, on the differences between spoken and written language, or further work following page 115, on describing a situation from another character's point of view.

Setting the homework
The children can take an anecdote from an adult or from their own experience for their written task. With an experience of their own, it helps them to empathise with others.

Back at school
Share re-written versions. Include some based on other anecdotes or experiences. Discuss how things can look very different from another person's point of view. Discuss what you have to do to see a situation from another point of view.

p117 THE MUMMERS' PLAY

Objective
Read, rehearse and modify performance of poetry. (Y5, T3, T4)

Lesson context
This play is suitable for performance as it is written in verse. It fits with a class study of choral and performance poetry.

Setting the homework
If possible enlarge to A3 to make annotation easier. Explain that this is a scene from a traditional mummers' play. Read the short introduction with the children, and explain that the task is to think about how the play could be performed. The children should annotate the sheet with notes.

Back at school
Ask for a group of volunteers to present the play. Allow ten minutes for preparation, then ask the children to perform. The performances and improvisations could be further polished and performed to a wider audience, for example, another class, school assembly.

p118 PHANTOM OF DELIGHT

Objective
Explore the challenge of older literature through reading poems. (Y5, T3, T6)

Lesson context
This homework could be integrated into a study of William Wordsworth, or a general exploration of older literature. The poem also provides an excellent example of character description.

Setting the homework
Explain that the poem is one of several that William Wordsworth wrote about a woman called Lucy. Encourage the children to read the poem aloud; it has a strong, almost song-like rhythm which will help them to access the meaning. The tasks will focus attention on the language and style of the poet. Ensure that terms *simile* and *metaphor* are secure.

Differentiation
There is some difficult vocabulary in this poem. Less able children could be given one of Wordsworth's shorter and simpler 'Lucy Poems'. Alternatively, they could simply read the poem with their helper to gain experience of older literature.

Back at school
Discuss Wordsworth's language and style.

p119 THE SECRET GARDEN

Objective
Explore the challenge of older literature through reading extracts from classic serials. (Y5, T3, T6, S6)

Lesson context
Use as part of a series of lessons on classic literature in different forms: prose, poetry and drama. If used with page 118, 'Phantom of delight', it provides a contrasting character description.

Setting the homework
Explain that the extract is the opening to the famous novel, *The Secret Garden*, first published in 1911. Ask the children if any of them have seen the story on television. Encourage them to read the passage aloud. It is written in long, complex sentences which will be more easily accessible if read aloud.

Differentiation
Helpers of less able children should first read the passage to their child and then re-read it with the child following or sharing the read.

Back at school
Discuss the character of Mary and the words and phrases the children have picked out. If some of the children have seen a televised version, ask them to say whether the description of Mary matches the character on TV.

p120 SHAKESPEARE'S LANGUAGE

Objective
Explore the challenge of older literature through discussing differences in language used. (Y5, T3, T6)

Lesson context
Some preparatory work on Shakespeare and other early dramatists should be done in Years 5/6 (Scottish P6/7). This might include watching the video of a Shakespeare or Marlowe play, reading re-tellings of stories and acting out some of the simpler scenes. Include a study of Shakespeare's language.

Setting the homework
Explain that the important thing is to read the text aloud. Shakespeare wrote these words to be performed, not to be read silently. Encourage the children to go further than substituting the glossary notes for the words in italics. They should simplify sentence construction.

Differentiation
Less able children should make a direct substitution of the glossary notes for the words in italics. You could prepare a version of the sheet in which this has already been done.

Back at school
Ask some of the more confident children to perform the scene.

p121 DESERT ISLAND

Objective
Write in the style of the author. (Y5, T3, T9)

Lesson context
Children can continue a scene at any point and this can be compared with what the author actually wrote. This homework could be used for doing the same task on any novel currently being studied.

Setting the homework
Ask the children to note the date when *Robinson Crusoe* was first published – it is more than a 100 years older than most other classics that they have read! They will notice at once the strangeness of the language, though such is Defoe's direct style, it is rarely a barrier to understanding. Emphasise that they should make up their own adventures for Robinson Crusoe.

Differentiation
Less able children could be given the same extract from a re-told version of the story. They will miss out on Defoe's language but will still be able to explore character and situation.

Back at school
Share the continuations and discuss how they might fit together to make a new, long *Robinson Crusoe* story. One possible follow-up would be to write that story, possibly in collaborative groups, each child writing a chapter to an agreed plan.

p122 MY DAD, YOUR DAD

Objective
Use performance poems as models for writing. (Y5, T3, T11)

Lesson context
This could form part of a series of lessons on oral and performance poetry along with pages 83 and 114.

Setting the homework
Explain to the children that the poem is a dialogue poem involving two characters. If they can work with a partner or helper, the activity will be more fun. They will need to use the poem as a model for their own writing. Emphasise that their poems do not have to rhyme and can be based on everyday conversation. They should then be prepared to recite/perform their poem in class.

Back at school
Talk about the poem on the sheet. Divide the class in half, each taking a part and recite the poem. Ask selected children to perform their poems.

p123 OLD SCHOOL FIELDS

Objective
Read examples of persuasive writing considering the deliberate use of ambiguity, half-truth, bias. (Y5, T3, T13)

Lesson context
Use with pages 124–127, as part of a series of homework activities that focus on argument and persuasion. This sheet is good preparation for writing a persuasive letter – one that avoids the mistakes made by Mr Rudge!

Setting the homework
Explain that the letter is typical of many persuasive letters that deliberately distort the truth in order to make a point. The task is to compare the statements in Mr Rudge's letter with the facts as shown on the plan. The reply from the council will be most effective if it politely answers Mr Rudge's points with reference to the facts.

Differentiation
Less able children may need help to see how Mr Rudge has distorted facts. This can be done by asking the parent/helper to compare the statements in the letter with the plan.

Back at school
Discuss Mr Rudge's letter. Ask: *Does he really have any grounds at all for complaint?* Share and discuss different letters of reply.

p124 ONE KID CRIME WAVE

Objective
Collect and investigate persuasive devices. (Y5, T3, T15)

Lesson context
Use with pages 123 and 125–127 as part of a series of homework activities that focus on argument and persuasion.

Setting the homework
The article contains good examples of persuasive devices. Go over the list so that the children understand what they are looking for.

Differentiation
Less able may need help to identify persuasive devices. More able should continue research into persuasive devices by looking at persuasive articles in newspapers and magazines.

Back at school
Collect from the children the persuasive devices they found.

p125 BOOK ADVERTISEMENT

Objective
Use persuasive devices. (Y5, T3, T15)

Lesson context
Use with pages 123–124 and 126–127, as part of a series of homework activities that focus on argument and persuasion. This sheet provides a good counterbalance to the others, as it includes visual persuasion. It is important that the children have read or nearly read a book which they can advertise.

Setting the homework
Discuss the illustration and blurb on the cover of the book which the children are going to advertise (or, if they are all different, discuss a good example). *How does the book cover appeal to the reader? How does the blurb get the reader interested?* Explain that they will be doing very similar things in their book advertisement, but must not simply copy the cover.

Differentiation
Such differentiation as may be needed should be provided by the book which the child has chosen to advertise.

Back at school
Display the advertisements around the classroom. Allow ten minutes browsing time, then discuss them: *Which ones most catch the attention and why? Do any miss out essential information?*

p126 BOREHAM SUPERTRAM

Objective
Write a letter to put a point of view. (Y5, T3, T17)

Lesson context
Use with pages 123–125 and 127, as part of a series of homework activities that focus on argument and persuasion.

Setting the homework
Explain that the children can use the information about the Boreham Supertram, or write about a real local issue. The important thing is that they carefully follow the format provided and write a series of well-presented arguments.

Differentiation
Less able children might concentrate on either: a) setting out a business letter, or b) writing an argument for or against an issue.

Back at school
Hold a debate about the Boreham Supertram so that the children can air their arguments. Mark the setting out of all the letters after the lesson.

p127 UNIFORM ARGUMENTS

Objective
Construct an argument in note form. (Y5, T3, T19)

Lesson context
Use with pages 123–126, as part of a series of homework activities that focus on argument and persuasion. This sheet focuses on preparing an argument in note form.

Setting the homework
Explain that half the battle of persuasive writing is thinking of good arguments. It is, therefore, a good idea to jot down all the arguments in note form first. Ask the children to use the arguments FOR school uniform to help them to think of arguments AGAINST.

Differentiation
None needed at this stage. The less able can often argue verbally quite well. It is when it comes to putting their arguments down in writing that support is needed.

Back at school
Use the notes as the basis for a class debate or discussion. This could be followed with a written task. The less able could write up one side of the argument as a short essay, whereas the more able could write a balanced essay in which they consider both sides of the argument and then reach a conclusion.

Look, cover, write, check (1)

- **Look** at each word in the first column, **cover** it up, **write** it in the second column, **check** it, then place a ✓ (correct) or a ✗ (wrong) after it.

Look	Write	Check	Look	Write	Check
abbreviation			convenient		
acceptable			courageous		
achieve			criticism		
amusement			deceive		
already			decision		
appropriate			definitely		
August			describe		
beautiful			description		
bicycle			disappear		
biscuit			disappoint		
breakfast			discipline		
brought			dissatisfied		
calculation			enough		
catalogue			especially		
ceiling			essential		
competition			excellent		

- Add words from your own writing that you need to learn.

Dear Helper,

Objective: to keep individual lists of words and learn to spell them.

Your child should be learning how to identify mis-spelled words and make lists of words to learn. Help them to find their spelling mistakes and add them to the list. Check that your child uses the **look, cover, write, check** method.

PHOTOCOPIABLE

More than one

Most nouns add **s** to form the plural, for example: **trees, houses**.
Words ending in **y** change to **ies** if the letter before **y** is a consonant,
for example: **fly, flies**.

- Look at the drawing and write the plural of the word in the box.

tree

house

school

motorway

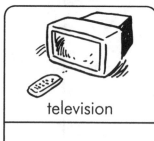

television

book

girl

film

- Now write the plurals of these in the empty box. One has been done for you.

dictionary

dictionaries

melody

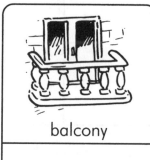

balcony

toy

holiday

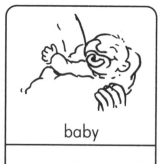

baby

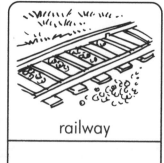

railway

fly

Dear Helper,

Objective: to learn the spelling pattern of –ies plurals.

If necessary, remind your child that *plural* means 'more than one'. When your child is completing the second list encourage them to think about every word, as three of them *should not* be changed to -ies.

Irregular plurals

Most words form their plural by adding **s**. However, there are a few **irregular** plurals. These fall into two groups:

1 Common English words, for example: **woman/women, sheep/sheep**.
   These do not usually cause spelling problems.
2 Words borrowed from Greek and Latin. These are often long and difficult words and need to be learned:
   • words ending in **– us** change to **i**: **radius/radii**
   • words ending in **– a** change to **ae**: **larva/larvae**
   • words ending in **– is** change to **es**: **oasis/oases**
   • words ending in **– um** change to **a**: **medium/media**

● Write the plurals of these common English words in the boxes.

deer

goose

ox

child

mouse

house

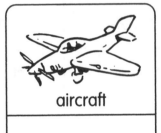
aircraft

man

● Now write out the plurals of these Greek and Latin-based words:

hippopotamus _____   crisis _____

terminus _____   diagnosis _____

stimulus _____   oasis _____

larva _____   aquarium _____

vertebra _____   gymnasium _____

● Add your own examples to this list on a separate sheet.

Dear Helper,

Objective: to learn the spellings of plurals that do not follow a regular pattern.
If necessary, remind your child that *plural* means 'more than one'. Help them to find the plural form by putting the words into sentences first and then applying the rules.

Prefix it!

Prefix Cards

auto	trans	tele	bi	circum
circum	auto	trans	tele	bi
bi	circum	auto	trans	tele
tele	bi	circum	auto	trans

Root Cards

graph	mit	scope	cycle	vent
ference	ography	parent	vision	plane
ceps	navigate	mobile	port	pathy
phone	sect	stance	matic	plant

- Cut out the cards, keeping them in two separate packs (**roots** and **prefixes**).
- Shuffle each pack so that the cards are mixed up and then place them face down.
- Pick up one card from each pack, trying to match a prefix card to a root card.
- Score one point for matching the cards and one point for saying what the word means. Use a dictionary to check.
- Score a bonus point for spelling the word when the cards have been turned over.

Dear Helper,

Objective: to find out about the meanings and spellings of words with the prefixes: *auto, bi, trans, tele, circum.*

Remind your child that a *root* is the basic part of a word to which letters (a *prefix*) can be added to the beginning to change its meaning. Play the game with your child following the rules. Encourage your child to look up words in a dictionary, learn their meanings and practise their spellings.

Ship synonyms

- Read the **synonyms** (words of similar meaning) of 'ship' in the first column.
- Add any others you can think of.
- Write a definition of each word in the second column.

Synonyms of 'ship'	Meanings
catamaran	a boat with two hulls
clipper	
cruise ship	
dinghy	
galleon	
galley	
hovercraft	
hydrofoil	
lifeboat	
submarine	
tanker	
trawler	
tug	
u-boat	
yacht	
Add your own synonyms.	

- Choose a suitable **synonym** from the list for these sentences:

 1 The oil _____ caused terrible pollution when it ran aground.

 2 A modern _____ can catch many tons of fish.

 3 The German _____ torpedoed the tanker.

 4 The warship of Greek and Roman times was called a _____.

 5 I learned to sail in a small _____.

Dear Helper,

Objective: to explain the differences between words of similar meaning.

Help your child to think of other *synonyms* for 'ship' (there are over 200!). If available, encourage your child to use a thesaurus and/or a dictionary to help.

Name:

Sleeping Beauty

- Read this version of *Sleeping Beauty*.
- Choose the most suitable **synonym** in brackets and highlight or underline it.
- Explain to your helper why you chose each synonym.

Prince Charming was a [good-looking/handsome/brave/charming] young [man/guy/youth/prince]. He heard that a [cute/beautiful/nice/pretty] princess was sleeping in a/n [ancient/old/impregnable/big] castle and could only be woken with a kiss. The problem was that the castle was protected by a [huge/prickly/thorny/big] hedge. The hedge was so [prickly/dangerous/high/perilous] that many knights had died trying to climb over it.

It was a [horrible/nasty/fearsome/scary] sight. The thorns were as big as [daggers/kitchen knives/dragon's teeth/rulers], and [skeletons/corpses/dead bodies/cadavers] hung from them. The air was filled with the [stench/pong/smell/aroma] of their rotting bodies.

But Prince Charming was not [scared/deterred/put off/frightened]. He walked [bravely/courageously/determinedly/quickly] towards the hedge and, to his amazement, the thorns turned to [beautiful/lovely/nice/pretty] flowers. That was because the 100-year spell ended at that moment – even though the prince knew nothing about it.

He walked [happily/eagerly/quickly/excitedly] to the castle where he found everybody [snoozing/sleeping/dozing/resting]. Then he found his way to Sleeping Beauty's tower. He had never seen anyone so [nice/sweet/cute/lovely]. Her skin was as pale as [milk/snow/paper/silk] and her lips were as red as [blood/roses/paint/lipstick].

He kissed her and she awoke with a [jerk/start/twitch/jump].

'What time is it?' she said [quietly/breathlessly/curiously/ sleepily].

'It's five and twenty past eight in the morning of March the first, 1492.'

'Oh, dear,' she [moaned/sighed/groaned/complained], 'that's much too early.' And she went back to sleep for another [2/10/100/1,000,000] years!

Dear Helper,

Objective: to explain the differences between words with similar meanings.
Check that your child has a good reason for each *synonym* chosen and that it is not repetitive (eg *prickly* in both sentences 3 and 4), inappropriate (eg *guy*), or boring (eg *nice*).

Name:

Word clusters

A **word cluster** is a group of words formed from the same root by adding different **prefixes** and **suffixes**. An example is given below for 'electric'.

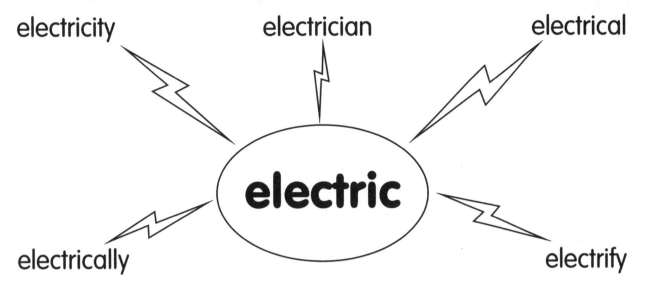

- Make word clusters for these words: **horror, know, profess, prophet, technical, sign.** Do the first below and then use the back of this sheet.

Extension

- Choose other words and make word clusters with them.

Dear Helper,

Objective: to identify root words, words derived from them and spelling patterns.

An awareness of *roots*, *prefixes* and *suffixes* helps with spelling and vocabulary. Remind your child of the following definitions: a *root* is the basic part of a word to which other parts can be added to change the meaning – a *prefix* at the beginning, a *suffix* at the end. Help your child to brainstorm all the possible variations of the given *root* words and to think of other words for which you can make word clusters.

A sitting duck

- Try to explain these common sayings and clichés.

Saying	Explanation
a sitting duck	
a square meal	
hit the nail on the head	
bury the hatchet	
blow your own trumpet	
let sleeping dogs lie	
the writing is on the wall	
under the weather	

- Add two more sayings and their explanations to the list.

Dear Helper,

Objective: to collect and explain a range of sayings and clichés.
These sayings are often well known to adults, but less so to children. Help your child to understand each saying by describing a situation in which it might be used. Help your child to think of other sayings.

Adverb attack

- Choose a suitable **adverb** from this list to use in the sentences below. Example: 'What a surprise!' said Sarah **excitedly**.

angrily	childishly	frostily	nervously	snappily
apologetically	coolly	grumpily	politely	softly
bluntly	crossly	hesitantly	proudly	spitefully
boastfully	deceitfully	hopefully	quietly	sulkily
brightly	eagerly	icily	sadly	sweetly
calmly	enthusiastically	loudly	scornfully	tactfully
cheekily	excitedly	miserably	sharply	wisely
cheerfully	frankly	moodily	shyly	wittily

'I'm not talking to you!' said Sally _____.

'I've just got to level 10 on that new computer game!' said Tim _____.

'My boyfriend has just finished with me,' said Zoe _____.

'I'm not taking any notice of you,' said the schoolboy _____.

'Perhaps it will stop raining,' said the tour guide _____.

'Shhh! You'll wake the baby,' said Mum _____.

'Well, how are we feeling today?' said the nurse _____.

'You look like you slept under a bus,' said Ashra _____.

Extension

- Choose three other **adverbs** from the list and use them in sentences of your own. Write them on the back of the sheet.

! **Remember:** use adverbs to improve dialogue in your own writing!

Dear Helper,

Objective: to use adverbs effectively when writing dialogue.

Remind your child that *adverbs* can tell us *how* a person is thinking or feeling when they say something. Read the *adverbs* and discuss in what situations they would be used. Encourage your child to think carefully when choosing the *adverbs*.

PHOTOCOPIABLE

Add an adverb

- Read the list of **verbs** and the **adverbs** that go with them.
- Add other suitable adverbs in the **'your adverb'** column.

Verb	Adverb	Your adverb
acted	rashly	suddenly
answered	correctly	
decided	reluctantly	
explained	clearly	
listened	attentively	
ran	quickly	
sang	sweetly	
shone	brightly	
slept	soundly	
smiled	happily	
spoke	sadly	
thought	deeply	
trembled	nervously	
walked	slowly	

Extension

- Write sentences using five of the verbs and adverbs. Use the back of the sheet.

Dear Helper,

Objective: to understand how adverbs can be used with verbs to make writing more descriptive.

If necessary, remind your child that a *verb* is a word that names an action and an *adverb* is a word that describes a *verb*. Help your child by giving examples of situations in which the given verbs and adverbs might be used together. If they need help thinking of extra *adverbs* for column three, ask questions such as: *If you were worried about something, how would you sleep?*

Editing

- Proof-read this story by correcting mistakes in spelling, punctuation and grammar.
- Edit the story by improving the description. There are notes to help you. Use the back of this sheet or a separate piece of paper to re-write the story.

House of Horror

Chloe and Zoe were trembling with exitement as they went through the turnstile into the theme park.

    'What shall we do first said Chloe'?

    'What about the House of Horror?' said Zoe.

    'Oh look! There's a roller-coaster!' said Chloe.

    'Great! Lets go!' said Zoe.
They qued for twenty minutes until their turn came. The safety bars came down automatically over their shoulders and they were off.

    The ride begins with a slow climb at a steep angle. Then suddenly they sped downwards at great speed. Chloe screamed. Zoe yelled.

    The roller-coaster twisted sharply to the left, went up, then over in a loop-the-loop. Chloe groaned and Zoe was sick.

    Then there was a steep drop. Chloe felt that she had left her stomach behind and Zoe felt dizzy.

    Then the roller-coaster turnd upside down again Chloe's shoe falls off and Zoe lost her purse.

    At last the roller-coaster began to slow down. The girls were wrecked. The roller-coaster stopped.

    'That was great!' said Chloe.

    'Yeah,' said Zoe. 'Let's do it again!'

NOTES

spelling

punctuation

try some different synonyms of 'said' to bring out the girls' excitement.

punctuation

spelling

describe their feelings

grammar

Add more description, describing how the girls felt and how they reacted.

Add to the description of the roller coaster by adding sounds, sights, and so on.

spelling

grammar/punctuation

Add more description about how wrecked they were.

Dear Helper,

Objective: to proof-read and edit a piece of writing.

This activity will help your child to look critically at a piece of writing to see how it can be improved. This is a skill they should apply to their own writing. The notes will help your child find the mistakes and the sections that need more description. Discuss the suggestions for improving the story.

Indirect dinosaurs

- Read this playscript with a friend or adult.
- Underline the **reported speech**.

  Tip: look for the phrase 'N says/said...', or 'N says/said that...'
  (N = the name of a person or a personal pronoun).

The scene: *A school corridor. Joe and Flo are coming back*
to the classroom after delivering the register to the secretary's office.

Joe: You won't believe what happened to me yesterday.

Flo: Won't I?

Joe: Probably not. I told my sister and she said my imagination was working overtime.

Flo: OK. Try me. My mum says I live in an imaginary world most of the time anyway.

Joe: Well, I was in the library reading this dinosaur book when all of a sudden it started to talk to me.

Flo: What? Have I heard this right? You say that the book you were reading was conversing with you?

Joe: Yes. I mean, not the book exactly, but one of the dinosaurs.

Flo: Oh sure. I think you, my friend, have been watching too many movies.

Joe: I know it sounds crazy, but it's true.

Flo: So, what did Dino have to say to you?

Joe: He said my choice of literature was excellent and thanked me for reading the book.

Flo: Why would he say that?

Joe: Because he said that as long as people read about dinosaurs, they won't ever really be extinct.

Flo: Not a daft diplo that Dino, eh? So what else did the old fossil have to say?

Just as he says this, Miss Scratchit, the headmistress, comes up.

Miss Scratchit: The old fossil says that the two of you had better get back to your classroom – NOW!

Dear Helper,

Objective: identify direct and indirect (reported) speech.

Take one or more of the parts and read the play with your child. Help them to find and underline the reported speech. Note, there is nothing difficult about *direct* and *reported* (or indirect) speech. Remind your child to look for the phrase 'says'/'said that'. Reported speech might also be indicated by other verbs which indicate speech, such as 'told', 'asked', 'shouted'. There is an example in the script.

Direct and reported

Direct speech uses words actually spoken. It is easy to recognise because it is shown by speech marks.

Reported (or indirect) speech is introduced by a phrase like **N said...** or **N said that...** (N = the name of a person). It states what was said rather than using the words that were actually spoken and speech marks are not used.

Rules for changing direct to reported speech:
Speech marks are not used.
Reporting clause is replaced by an introductory clause often ending with 'that'.
Often, the tense changes from present to past.
Personal pronouns change: first- and second-person pronouns become third-person pronouns.

- Change these examples of **direct speech** into **indirect speech**:

'My face feels all itchy,' said Sarah.

_____

'I'm only joking,' laughed Dad.

_____

'I don't want to stay out past midnight,' said Simon.

_____

'I'm not afraid of spiders,' said Sunil.

_____

- Change these examples of **indirect speech** into **direct speech**:

Tim said that he really hated going to the dentist.

_____

Zoe said that she was going to stay in to wash her hair.

_____

Joe shouted to the taxi driver to hurry up.

_____

Shona asked her mum if she could have a party.

_____

Dear Helper,

Objective: changing between direct and reported speech.
Help your child to apply the rules to the sentences. A good way to do this is to ask questions like: *What did Sarah say?* for the first set of questions, and: *What were Tim's actual words?* for the second set.

Punctuation pointers

Punctuation makes texts easier to read. Explore this in two steps in the following passages.

Step 1: No punctuation

- Read this passage aloud.

the problem was mondays every monday mum took katie
to the saddle club but because it was seven miles away she
didn't think it was worth coming home so she waited that
meant kimberley had to wait too and kimberley hated horses
she liked harleys much better harleys are american motorbikes
with high handlebars and low seats kimberley thought it would
be much more fun to ride a harley than a horse

- Say if reading it was easy or difficult and explain why.
- Rewrite the passage adding capital letters and full stops.
  Use the back of this sheet.

Step 2: Dialogue not punctuated or set out clearly

- Read this passage with someone else. One person should
  read Katie's lines and the other, Kimberley's lines.

I don't know what you see in horses. They're stupid!
said Kimberley. They're better than Harley's anyway,
replied Katie. You can't go a hundred miles an hour
on a horse! You can't jump on a Harley! There no
brakes on a horse, they're dangerous! The're safer
than Harleys! Well, horses go lame! So what. Harleys
go rusty and fall to pieces and get sent to the scrap yard!

- Say if reading it was easy or difficult and explain why.
- Write out the above passage with speech marks.
  Start a new indented line for each change of speaker.
  Use the back of this sheet.

Dear Helper,

Objective: to understand the need for punctuation.

As children develop an appreciation of punctuation, their ability to use it effectively is increased. Listen while
your child reads the passage in Step 1 and share in the reading of the passage in Step 2. Help with punctuating
both passages. Encourage re-reading of the passages to check that all punctuation has been included.

Old new school

Dialogue is set out with a new indented line for each change of speaker.
It is punctuated with speech marks.
A capital letter is used after the first speech mark.
A comma, question mark or exclamation mark is used before the final speech mark.

- Use different coloured pens to highlight:
  - the new indented lines which show the changes of speaker;
  - the speech marks; and
  - the other punctuation marks.

The building was at least a hundred years old. The windows
were arched, like a church's, and the woodwork was full of wormholes.
It looked more like a set for a horror film than a school.

'I'm not going in!' said Simon.

'But you have to,' said his mum, patiently. 'It's the law. Every child has to go
to school.'

'But it looks haunted!' wailed Simon.

'Nonsense!' snapped his mum. 'You've been watching too many horror films.'

She took Simon to the door and watched him go in. He crept down the gloomy
corridor, wondering where to go, when a harsh voice snapped, 'You, boy, get into the
classroom at once!'

Simon turned round and to his horror he saw a teacher dressed in a
mortar-board cap, black gown and long skirt – the way teachers dressed
a hundred years ago! He was too frightened to speak, and did as he was told.
What he saw in the classroom was even worse: thirty children
in Victorian clothes all sat in neat rows. He was right. This was
a haunted school, and these children were all ghosts!

'Sit down!' snapped his teacher.

It was all too much for Simon. He ran to the open
window and shouted, 'Mum, come back! The school's
full of Victorian ghosts!'

Then he felt a hand on his shoulder. Trembling he
turned round. It was the teacher.

'Don't be frightened,' she said in a kind voice. 'We're
having our Victorian day today as part of our history project!'

- Leave out the last two lines and write a different ending to the story, including
  several lines of dialogue. Use the back of this sheet.

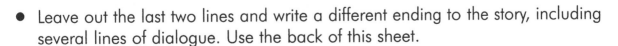

Dear Helper,

Objective: to understand how speech is set out and punctuated.
Ask your child to read the passage aloud to you. Help them to identify and highlight indented lines, speech marks and other punctuation using different colour pens. Discuss ideas for continuing the story.

PHOTOCOPIABLE

Name:

Is it simple?

Auxiliary verbs are 'helper' verbs which are used to form certain tenses. This is shown clearly in the table below.

	Simple	**Continuous**
Present	The present simple is used for things happening now, eg The chicken crosses the road and actions that happen on a regular basis, eg I clean my teeth every day.	The present continuous is formed with the **auxiliary verb** 'to be' + the '-ing' form of the verb. It is used for an event which is in progress, eg I am writing a book.
Past	The past simple is used for an event which has taken place at a definite time in the past, eg She left yesterday.	The past continuous is formed with the **auxiliary verb** 'to be' + the '-ing' form of the verb. It is used for an event which was in progress in the past for a period of time, eg I was walking to school.

- Decide whether each of these sentences is **present** or **past, simple** or **continuous,** then copy it into the correct box above:

I am learning French.

Sally talks very quickly.

It was raining heavily.

She cried when she heard the news.

I hope he gets better.

I am walking as fast as I can.

The car stopped at the red light.

They were arguing all night.

Dear Helper,

Objective: to investigate how different tenses are formed by using auxiliary verbs.

Help your child to understand the difference between present, past, simple and continuous using the table and the examples. Help your child to sort the sentences. Sort for past and present first, then simple and continuous.

Which person?

The best way to understand **person** is to look at the verb 'to be' written out in full:

To be (past tense)

Person	Singular	Plural
First person:	I was	we were
Second person:	you were	you were
Third person:	name/he/she/it was	they were

The first and third person forms are used to create the 'point of view' in story writing. The second person is used rarely, but may be found in adventure game books and computer games.

- Read these story beginnings and say which person they are written in (first, second or third).

Dougie the dragon was hungry. No tourists had visited his castle for many years. It was time to put an advertisement in the paper.

Person_____

My name is Edward. I am the only survivor of the *SS Albatross* – the only person alive who can tell of the terrible things that happened as she sank below the freezing waves last December.

Person_____

Dear Diary,
This is my second night in the Hotel Transylvania and my host has been very kind to me. Indeed, he has invited me to a feast tomorrow night and he has promised to introduce me to all his friends. He says that I will be the main attraction. I can't wait until tomorrow!

Person_____

You are the officer on duty on the bridge of the *RMS Titanic*. It is night. The sea is calm and perfectly flat. There is no moon and the stars are shining brilliantly. It is chilly – about 32 degrees Farenheit. You are travelling at 21 knots into the darkness. Suddenly you hear a cry from able seaman Fleet in the crow's nest: 'Iceberg right ahead!' What will you do?

Person_____

Dear Helper,

Objective: to identify viewpoint in written texts.

Help your child to relate the explanation of the verb to the texts. If your child needs further support, remind them that 'I' or 'we' usually indicates that the story is autobiographical or that one of the characters is telling the story in the first person. 'He' or 'she' indicates the author is telling the story from a third-person perspective. 'You' indicates a second-person narrative, where the reader is the one being written about.

S

Name:

Video phone

- Act out making a video phone call by following the instructions below.
- Underline the **imperative** forms of the verb. (bossy)
- Write instructions for using an everyday object, eg a fire extinguisher.

DO NOT TRY TO MAKE A VIDEO CALL TO A PERSON WHO DOES NOT HAVE A VIDEO PHONE.

VIDEO

AUDIO

① **SELECT VIDEO OR AUDIO.**

② **INSERT 20P, 50P, £1 OR £2 COINS (50p MINIMUM), OR SWIPE YOUR CRDIT CARD THROUGH THE SLOT.**

③ **DIAL THE NUMBER.**

④ **IF YOU ARE MAKING A VIDEO CALL, MAKE SURE YOU LOOK DIRECTLY AT THE CAMERA (MARKED WITH A BLACK BUTTON)**

⑤ **WHEN YOU HEAR A SERIES OF BEEPS, INSERT MORE COINS OR END YOUR CONVERSATION.**

⑥ **PRESS THE WHITE BUTTON FOR A RECEIPT AFTER A CREDIT CARD CALL.**

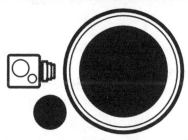

Dear Helper,

Objective: to identify the imperative form (direct order) in instructions.

Help your child to role play making the call. Do this by pretending to be on the receiving end. Help your child to identify the *imperative verb*. Remind your child that imperative sentences give orders and usually begin with the verb that commands.

PHOTOCOPIABLE

100 LITERACY HOMEWORK ACTIVITIES • YEAR 5 TERM 1

Beginnings

There are many ways of starting a story, eg description of a place or person, dialogue, writing in the first person ('I'), beginning with an exciting event.

- Look at the beginnings of these well-known books and decide which one of the beginnings listed above they are using.
- Explain what it is about the beginning of each that makes you want to read on.

Dark spruce forest frowned on either side of the frozen waterway. The trees had been stripped by a recent wind of their white covering of frost, and they seemed to lean toward each other, black and ominous, in the fading light. A vast silence reigned over the land. (from *White Fang* by Jack London)

This beginning uses _____

I want to read on because _____

Look out, Willie – the canal...!' Super Gran yelled, as she Super-sprinted across the uneven cobblestones of the towpath towards the boy, her grandson Willard, to save him from a watery grave. (from *Super Gran Rules OK!* by Forrest Wilson)

This beginning uses _____

I want to read on because _____

A long time ago, when I was young, on a Wednesday afternoon, a very strange thing happened to me, so strange, you probably won't believe it. That's up to you. Anyway, this is what happened. *(from Princess by Mistake by Penelope Lively)*

This beginning uses _____

I want to read on because _____

Deep in the night, thunder crashed in the dark, leaden skies over Transylvania. Brilliant flashes of fork lightening lit up the jagged mountain and the wicked, hideously shaped Castle Duckula, which perched precariously on its summit. (from *Duckula and the Ghost Train Mystery* by John Broadhead)

This beginning uses _____

I want to read on because _____

'I'm going shopping in the village,' George's mother said to George on Saturday morning. 'So be a good boy and don't get up to mischief.'
   This was a silly thing to say to a small boy at any time – it immediately made him wonder what sort of mischief he might get up to. (from *George's Marvellous Medicine* by Roald Dahl)

This beginning uses _____

I want to read on because _____

Dear Helper,

Objective: to compare different story beginnings and talk about what makes a good story beginning.

Read the story beginnings with your child and discuss their characteristics, eg what type is it? what makes you want to read on? If possible, help your child to find other examples.

Phrenological characters

In the 19th century, many people believed that it was possible to read a person's character by the bumps on their head. This so-called 'science' was called *phrenology*. A person who practised the science was called a *phrenologist*.

- Imagine you are a phrenologist. Where would you expect to find the bumps on the head of the character you have been reading about? Colour them in on the diagram below.
- Write a paragraph describing the character using the words in the areas you shaded. You can use the back of this sheet.

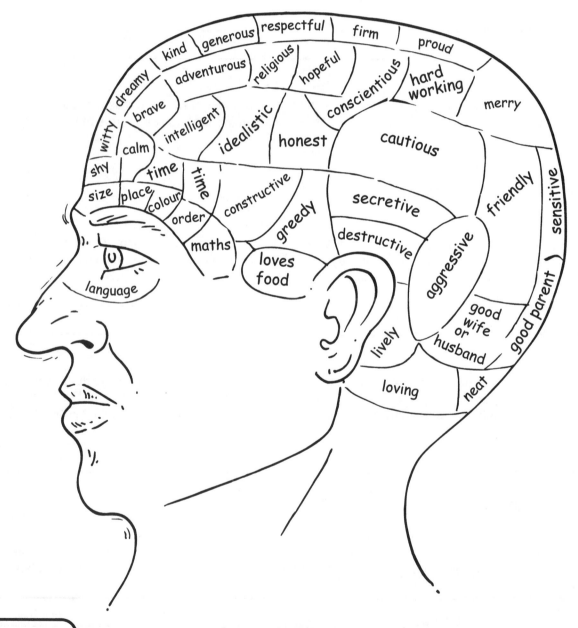

Dear Helper,

Objective: to investigate characters in stories.

Discuss the idea of phrenology with your child. For fun, and as a way of becoming familiar with the diagram, try to read the bumps on each other's heads. Ask your child about the character they have been reading about and discuss which bumps on the diagram should be shaded in.

Mrs May

- Read this extract from *The Borrowers* by Mary Norton.
- Highlight or underline words and phrases that help us to get to know the character of Mrs May. Use one colour for what she says, another for what she does, and another for the author's descriptions.

It was Mrs May who first told me about them. No, not me. How could it have been me – a wild, untidy, self-willed little girl who stared with angry eyes and was said to crunch her teeth? Kate, she should have been called. Yes, that was it, Kate. Not that the name matters much either way: she barely comes into the story.

Mrs May lived in two rooms in Kate's parents' house in London. She was, I think, some kind of relation. Her bedroom was on the first floor, and her sitting-room was a room which, as part of the house, was called 'the breakfast-room'. Now 'breakfast-rooms' are all right in the morning when the sun streams in on the toast and marmalade, but by afternoon they seem to vanish a little and to fill with a strange silvery light, their own twilight; there is a kind of sadness in them then, but as a child it was a sadness Kate liked. She would creep in to Mrs May just before tea-time and Mrs May would teach her to crochet.

Mrs May was old, her joints were stiff, and she was – not strict exactly, but she had that inner certainty which does instead. Kate was never 'wild' with Mrs May, nor untidy, nor self-willed; and Mrs May taught her many things besides crochet: how to wind wool into an egg-shaped ball; how to run-and-fell and plan a darn; how to tidy a drawer and to lay, like a blessing, above the contents, a sheet of rustling tissue against the dust.

'Why so quiet, child?' asked Mrs May one day, when Kate was sitting hunched and idle upon the hassock. 'What's the matter with you? Have you lost your tongue?'

'No,' said Kate, pulling at her shoe button, 'I've lost the crochet hook . . .' (they were making a bedquilt – in woollen squares: there were thirty still to do). 'I know where I put it,' she went on hastily; 'I put it on the bottom shelf of the book-case just beside my bed.'

'On the bottom shelf?' repeated Mrs May, her own needle flicking steadily in the firelight. 'Near the floor?'

'Yes,' said Kate, 'but I looked on the floor. Under the rug. Everywhere. The wool was still there though. Just where I'd left it.'

'Oh dear,' exclaimed Mrs May lightly, 'don't say they're in this house too!'

'That what are?' asked Kate.

'The Borrowers,' said Mrs May, and in the half light she seemed to smile.

- Write about the different things you have learned about Mrs May.

Dear Helper,

Objective: to find out how characters are presented through dialogue, action and description.

Read this passage with your child. Discuss the character of Mrs May and help your child pick out the different ways in which she is described.

Name:

Pleasant Sounds

- Read John Clare's poem about his everyday experiences of sights and sounds.

John Clare's experiences

The rustling of leaves under the feet in woods
   and under hedges;
The crumping of cat-ice and snow down wood-rides,
   narrow lanes, and every street causeway;
Rustling through a wood or rather rushing, while the
   wind halloos in the oak– top like thunder;
The rustle of birds' wings startled from their nests or
   flying unseen into the bushes;
The whizzing of larger birds overhead in a wood,
   such as crows, puddocks, buzzards;
The trample of robins and woodlarks on the brown
   leaves, and the patter of squirrels on the green moss;
The fall of an acorn on the ground, the pattering of
   nuts on the hazel branches as they fall from
   ripeness;
The flirt of the groundlark's wing from the stubbles –
   how sweet such pictures on dewy mornings,
   when the dew flashes from its brown feathers!

- Write about your everyday experiences of sights and sound. Use the back of this sheet.
- Make a list of the differences between your experiences and John Clare's.

Dear Helper,

Objective: to consider how writers write about their own experience.
Read the poem with your child, then discuss each sentence or phrase and of what it reminds you both.

Computer kids

- Read the playscript below and highlight some examples of the following: **cast list, scene descriptions, performance notes in brackets, text in italics, character names, colons, lines of dialogue.**

Cast: Mr Beetham (the class teacher); The Improvers Group of pupils: Ryan, Robert, Tracy, Trudy; Mrs Scratchit (the headmistress).

Scene 1: *Mr Beetham's classroom. On the teacher's desk is a gleaming new computer. The Improvers Group are gathered around the table.*

Mr Beetham: Today we are going to have our first lesson
Robert: in...er...ICT.
Tracy: What's that, Sir?
Trudy: (*Hissing with scorn*) Computers, idiot!
Mr Beetham: Sir, I didn't know you were an expert in computers!
(*Uncertainly*) Well, Mrs Scratchit said that I had to get
myself up to date. She sent me on a computer
course so that I could teach you lot all about them.

Mr Beetham starts his lesson. After much fiddling around, he manages to switch the computer on. The computer boots up and the screen fills with icons.

Mr Beetham: Now, I've stuck the boot in - I mean, booted up. The
next step is to take the...er...moose...
All: MOUSE!
Mr Beetham: (*Jumping up and looking round*) Where! (*Then realising his mistake*) Take the...er...mouse...and point it at the er...
Tracy: Icon?
Mr Beetham: Er...icon...yes. Then...er...why is nothing happening?
Ryan: You have to click it, Sir.
Trudy: Double click it.

Mr Beetham taps the mouse with his fingernail. The Improvers Group groan.

Robert: Like this, Sir. (*Ryan takes over.*) Then the program
opens. This is a word processor.
Tracy: The next thing is to enter text, like this.
Trudy: (*She types.*)
Ryan: You can cut and paste. (*She demonstrates.*)
You can even add graphics. (*He demonstrates.*)

At that moment, Mrs Scratchit walks into the classroom.

Mrs Scratchit: Well, Mr Beetham, I must compliment you on the progress
of your pupils. You didn't need to go on that course
after all. You are obviously an expert
on computers!

Dear Helper,

Objective: to understand features of playscripts.
Read this play with your child. You could each take several parts. Help to identify the different features.

Meg Merrilies

- Read this poem by John Keats.
- Underline all the descriptive words and phrases.
- Highlight the words that rhyme.

Old Meg she was a Gipsy,
And lived upon the Moors;
Her bed it was the brown heath turf,
And her house was out of doors.

Her apples were swart blackberries,
Her currants, pods o' broom;
Her wine was dew of the wild white rose
Her book a churchyard tomb.

Her Brothers were the craggy hills,
Her Sisters larchen trees;
Alone with her great family
She lived as she did please.

No breakfast had she many a morn,
No dinner many a noon,
And, 'stead of supper, she would stare
Full hard against the moon.

But every morn, of woodbine fresh
She made her garlanding,
And, every night, the dark glen Yew
She wove, and she would sing.

And with her fingers, old and brown,
She plaited Mats o' Rushes,
And gave them to the cottagers
She met among the bushes.

Old Meg was brave as Margaret Queen
And tall as Amazon;
An old red blanket cloak she wore,
A chip hat had she on.
God rest her aged bones somewhere!
She died full long agone!

John Keats

Dear Helper,

Objective: to read a poem by a major poet.
Read this poem taking verses in turn. Discuss any archaic and unfamiliar vocabulary. Help your child to pick out descriptive words and phrases and identify rhyming words.

Name:

Poetry analyser

● Use this writing frame to help you write about the poem your teacher has given you.

Subject: Say briefly what the poem is about.

Theme: Explain the ideas that are expressed in the poem.

Form: Describe the form of the poem.
Is it written in verses; if so, how many lines
in each verse?

What rhyme scheme is used?

Write it out using letters of the alphabet.

How many stressed syllables in
each line (count the first four lines)?

Are the lines long or short?

Is there a regular pattern?

Style: Look for unusual and interesting words. Jot some down and explain why they are effective.

Look for figures of speech, eg similes and metaphors. Write down one or two and explain them.

Dear Helper,

Objective: to explore the style, form and theme of a poem.
Your child should have used a writing frame like this before. Read together the poem your child has brought
home. Discuss how to complete each section and share your own responses.

Wild witches' ball

Rhyme occurs when words end with the same (or similar) sound. Rhymes are usually placed at the end of lines of poetry,
  eg *end* and *mend* are rhymes.

Internal rhyme occurs when a word in a line rhymes with the word at the end of a line,
  eg Now Robin *Hood* was both brave and *good*.

Alliteration occurs when words begin with the same sound,
  eg They **st**ruck him with **st**icks and with **st**ones.

- Read the poem and highlight or underline in three different colours:
  rhyme, **internal rhyme** and **alliteration**.

late last night at wildwitchhall
we witches held our wild witch ball.
in every size and shape and weight
we witches came to celebrate.

ten tall crones with moans and groans
battled in barrels with bats and bones.
nine queer dears with pointed ears
dangled and swang from the chandeliers.

witches eight with mangy tresses
danced with seven sorceresses.
witches six in shaggy rags
played toss and tag with five old hags.

four fat bags took healthy bites
from parts of three unsightly frights.
two fierce furies dug a ditch
and tumbled in one lumpy witch.

there were witches squeezed in every nook
whichever where you cared to look.
how many witches can you see
at our annual wildwitch witches' spree?

Jack Prelutsky

Dear Helper,

Objective: to consider the impact of sound patterns in poetry: rhyme and alliteration.
Read the poem with your child, taking verses in turn. Encourage your child to hear and enjoy the effects of sound.

Name:

Word play

- Read and enjoy these poems, then highlight the words which are 'played' with by the poet.

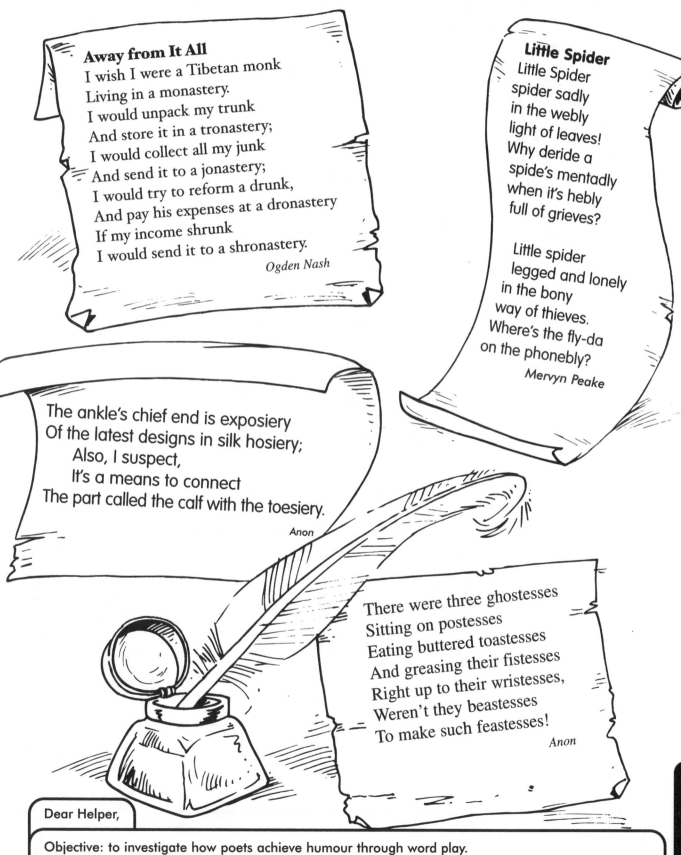

Away from It All
I wish I were a Tibetan monk
Living in a monastery.
I would unpack my trunk
And store it in a tronastery;
I would collect all my junk
And send it to a jonastery;
I would try to reform a drunk,
And pay his expenses at a dronastery
If my income shrunk
I would send it to a shronastery.

Ogden Nash

Little Spider
Little Spider
spider sadly
in the webly
light of leaves!
Why deride a
spide's mentadly
when it's hebly
full of grieves?

Little spider
legged and lonely
in the bony
way of thieves.
Where's the fly-da
on the phonebly?

Mervyn Peake

The ankle's chief end is exposiery
Of the latest designs in silk hosiery;
    Also, I suspect,
    It's a means to connect
The part called the calf with the toesiery.

Anon

There were three ghostesses
Sitting on postesses
Eating buttered toastesses
And greasing their fistesses
Right up to their wristesses,
Weren't they beastesses
To make such feastesses!

Anon

Dear Helper,

Objective: to investigate how poets achieve humour through word play.
Take it in turns with your child to read the poems and then talk about how each one plays with words.

The Gipsy Laddie

- Read the ballad.
- Add some new scenes, eg introducing the Gipsy Laddie or showing how the lady goes from riches to poverty. Keep to the same verse form if you can; otherwise write your ideas in prose. Use the back of the sheet.

It was late at night when the Squire came home
Enquiring for his lady.
His servant made a sure reply:
'She's gone with the gipsy Davy.'

     Rattle turn a gipsy gipsy
     Rattle turn a gipsy Davy.

'O go catch up my milk-white steed,
The black one's not so speedy,
I'll ride all night till broad daylight,
Or overtake my lady.'

He rode and he rode till he came to the town,
He rode till he came to Barley.
The tears came rolling down his cheeks,
And then he spied his lady.

'It's come, go back, my dearest dear,
Come, go back, my honey;
It's come, go back, my dearest dear,
And you'll never lack for money.'

'I won't go back, my dearest dear,
I won't go back, my honey;
For I wouldn't give a kiss from gipsy's lips
For you and all your money.'

She soon wore out her finery,
Her velvet shoes and stockings;
The gold ring off her finger's gone
The gold braid off her clothing.

'Once I had a house and I had land
A feather-bed and money;
But now I've come to an old straw pad
With the gipsies dancing round me.'

Anon

Dear Helper,

Objective: to write new scenes or characters in the style of the writer.

Read the ballad so that each of you reads the dialogue of one of the characters. Talk about the kind of scenes that could be added to the poem.

Name:

T

The poetry processor

Write three adjectives describing the subject of the poem.	Write three words which sum up the emotions aroused by the subject of the poem.
Write a simile to describe the subject of the poem.	Describe a landscape that would be a good backdrop for the subject of your poem.
Write a simile to describe the subject of your poem, then cross out 'like'. (You have written a metaphor!)	Write a line which contains a verb which is something the subject of your poem might do.
Talk to your subject as though it were human. (You have added personification!)	Write three adverbs to go with any of the verbs you have used.
What does the subject of your poem make you think about?	What mood does the subject of your poem put you in?
Find the best line you have written so far and repeat it.	Write a line about something which is the opposite of your subject.
Say how you feel about the subject of your poem.	If the subject of your poem were music, what would it sound like?
Write three words which you associate with the subject of your poem.	Think of something completely different to your subject and try to compare it with the subject in a simile.

- Cut out these cards, shuffle them, then pick them up at random to give you ideas for writing lines for a poem.
- Redraft your poem by choosing your best lines, placing them in the best order and writing extra lines, where necessary.

Dear Helper,

Objective: to write a poem conveying feelings, reflections or moods.
You can help your child by making this poetry-writing game fun. Help your child with ideas. You could also help by writing a poem yourself.

PHOTOCOPIABLE

100 LITERACY HOMEWORK ACTIVITIES • YEAR 5 TERM 1

Bedtime blues

- Turn this dialogue into a playscript.
- Add notes to help with the production of the scene.

! **Remember!** Use all the appropriate conventions: cast list, scene descriptions, performance notes in brackets.

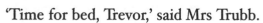

'Time for bed, Trevor,' said Mrs Trubb.

'Aw, Mum, can't I stay up a bit longer?' said Trevor.

'No you can't! It's school tomorrow.'

'But Trish is still up.'

'I'm older than you. I'm allowed to stay up 'till ten,' said Trish.

'What about Dad? He stays up really late!'

'That's because I'm on the 4.00 o'clock shift,' snapped Dad.

'You're lucky!'

'No, I'm not. Shift work is exhausting. You want to get yourself a good education so that you can work proper hours.'

'Come on, Trevor,' said Mum.

'Can I listen to my CD player in bed, then?'

'He shouldn't be listening to his CDs – he hasn't even done his homework yet,' said Trish.

'What!' screamed Dad.

'Well, Trevor' said Mum, 'it looks like you'll be staying up later after all!'

'No, please, Mum – I'm really tired!'

'Come on, Trevor. What have you got to do?'

'History,' said Trish.

'Be quiet!' snapped Trevor.

'Get your books out.'

'Mum, I'm tired. I should be in bed! I've got school tomorrow.'

'There!' said Trish, 'I've put all his books on the table!'

'You!' hissed Trevor.

'That'll teach you to stay up past your bedtime!' said Trish.

Dear Helper,

Objective: to write a playscript including production notes, from a given conversation.

Read through the dialogue and help your child to rewrite it as a play. Don't forget to add scene descriptions and indicate how lines should be spoken. If available, use a playscript as a model.

Name:

The haunted house

- Read the playscript.
- Add stage directions and performance notes to the script.
- Make up another scene with the same characters. Use the back of this sheet.

Joanne: I'm scared, Tanya. Let's go home.

Tanya: Don't be a wimp, Joanne. You're still not worrying about ghosts, are you? There are no such things as ghosts. Here's the place. Let me switch the torch on. Does the light make you feel better?

Joanne: But we should be at your house. My mum will be really mad if she knows we're here.

Tanya: Oh, for goodness sake, stop fussing! Our houses are only over the road. We can soon run back. It's an adventure.

Joanne: I don't like adventures. This place has been empty for years. It could be dangerous, and I've heard people say that it's haunted.

Tanya: Look! The back door's open. Let's go in.

Joanne: It's spooky in here, Tanya. So dark and quiet. Where are you? Can I hold your hand?

Tanya: There's nothing in here to be scared of. Nothing at all, apart from an old couch. No ghosts. Nothing.

Joanne: Listen to that noise! What is it? It's coming from the other room. It must be the ghost!

Tanya: And it's coming closer! Quick – behind the couch! I'll turn off the torch. Lie still!

Joanne: It's the ghost. I know it is. It's coming to get us!

Tanya: I've got to see what it is.

Joanne: Look Tanya – it's a cat! Only a cat.

Tanya: There's your ghost, Joanne. A poor hungry cat. Let's take it home. Come on, Ghostie. We'll give you some milk. Nice Ghostie.

Dear Helper,

Objective: to annotate a playscript as a preparation for performance.

Read the playscript, sharing the parts with your child. Discuss how the play could best be staged and use this discussion as a way of helping your child to add stage directions and performance notes.

Lusitania recount

- Using different coloured pens, highlight or underline the following features in this **recount** text: introduction, chronological order, past tense, temporal connectives (linking words to do with time), action focused.
  Complete one feature at a time.

The *Lusitania* disaster of 1915 was like an action replay of the *Titanic* disaster of three years earlier. The two ships even looked alike, both having four tall funnels and two tall masts fore and aft.

The *Lusitania* sailed from New York to Liverpool with a full load of passengers, including Canadian soldiers, and a cargo of munitions. She was the largest liner afloat at the time (though smaller than the *Titanic*). She was also the holder of the transatlantic speed record. She was much faster than any German U-boat so it was believed that if she kept moving, there would be little danger. Just after 2:00 pm on May 7, the ship changed course toward the Irish Sea and the coast of Ireland came into view. Suddenly, a warning was shouted from the bridge, 'There is a torpedo coming, Sir!'

Soon after, there was a violent explosion in the *Lusitania* hull. It was a direct hit from a German submarine about 700 yards away. The ship sank so quickly that most lifeboats could not be lowered in time. Within 18 minutes the liner had gone down. 1198 of the 1959 passengers died – almost as many as died in the *Titanic* disaster.

The German captain, after watching the disaster through his periscope, wrote in his log, 'The ship stops immediately and quickly heels to starboard. Great confusion… Lifeboats being cleared and lowered to water. Many boats crowded… immediately fill and sink.'

The German government said that the ship had been sunk because it was carrying soldiers and munitions. However, public opinion was outraged, and it was one of the reasons why America eventually joined the war against Germany.

Extension

- The extract from the German captain's log book is different in style.
  What are the differences? (**Hint!** Look for: tense, sentence structure.)

Dear Helper,

Objective: to identify the features of recounted texts.
Remind your child that a 'recount' text is one that is written to retell for information or entertainment. Read the text with your child, then help them to find and highlight examples of the different features.

100 LITERACY HOMEWORK ACTIVITIES • YEAR 5 TERM 1

Name:

Failed Flying 10

- Read the bicycle safety report.
- Using different coloured pens, highlight or underline the following features in this report: **data** (ie facts and figures), use of **present tense, explanations, conclusion.**

Bicycle Safety Report	
Model, Type and Date	Flying 10, Tourer, 1998
Name of Owner	Patricia Trubb
Tyres	Only .5mm tread depth. Should be changed soon. Both tyres underinflated.
Brakes	Front brake blocks badly worn. Rear brake blocks partly worn. All brake blocks should be replaced. Brake cable rusty. Needs replacing.
Lights, reflectors and bell	Lights not working. New dynamo needed. Rear reflector cracked. Both should be replaced immediately – bike ILLEGAL. Bell works.
Frame	Sound. All nuts and bolts tight. Some surface rust in places, but nothing that would cause structural weakness.
Accessories	Rear pannier bag catching in spokes. Remove.
Result	FAIL
Recommendation	Owner should stop using the bike immediately. However, a small amount of money spent on replacement items will turn this into a good safe bike once again.
Signature	S. Panna

- Write a report on your own bicycle, or on another household item.

Newfoundland notes

- Read this description of Newfoundland.
- Make notes using the format below which is designed to stop you writing full sentences.
- Look at the map and make a few notes.
- Write a short paragraph from your notes. Use the back of the sheet.

The Vikings were the first to discover this large island in about the year 1000. They called it Vinland. In 1497, the island was rediscovered by John Cabot, who called it the 'new foundelande.' One hundred years later, in 1583, England claimed it as its first overseas colony. At that time St John's, now the capital city, was a flourishing settlement. The city is near to the Grand Banks, which are the world's richest fishing grounds, and has the best natural harbour in the country. In 1948, Newfoundland voted to join Canada as its tenth province.

The island has an area of 156 185 square miles and a population of approximately 600 000. The lowest average temperatures in the St John's area are -30.3 °C in January, and the highest are 16.2 °C. More than 90% of the land area is covered by forest. The main industries are forestry and fishing.

Notes (words or phrases)	Numbers (where appropriate)
Discovered by Vikings	About 1000

Dear Helper,

Objective: to make notes and build on these in writing.

Encourage your child to read the text and study the map. Check that the notes in the first column are words and phrases only, NOT full sentences.

Name:

Abbreviations

Abbreviations are useful in note-taking and many are accepted in ordinary texts. Note that full stops are often used after abbreviations, though they are omitted in very common abbreviations, such as Mr, Dr and BBC.

- Write the meaning of the **abbreviations** (Abbr.) in the **meanings** column. The first one is done for you.
- Try to find more abbreviations and write them on the back of this sheet.

Abbr.	Meanings	Abbr.	Meanings
&	and	km	
£		Mon.	
Ave.		Mr	
BA		Ms	
BBC		pm	
Beds.		Rd	
Blvd.		Sgt.	
cm		SOS	
Co.		St.	
DJ		UHF	
Dr		vol.	
FM		YHA	
g		Yorks.	

Dear Helper,

Objective: use simple abbreviations
Help your child find the meanings of the more difficult abbreviations by using a dictionary. Then, help your child find more examples of abbreviations, preferably used in a real context, such as newspapers and magazines.

Look, cover, write, check (2)

- **Look** at each word in the first column, **cover** it up, **write** it in the second column, **check** it, then place a ✓ (correct) or a ✗ (wrong) after it.

Look	Write	Check	Look	Write	Check
except			irrelevant		
exercise			irritable		
existence			judge		
extremely			knowledge		
fought			leisure		
February			library		
government			likeable		
guard			lovable		
guess			maintain		
height			maintenance		
humorous			manageable		
humour			marriage		
immediate			minute		
immediately			mischief		
independent			misspelled		
insistent			naive		
instalment			naughty		

- Add words from your own writing that you need to learn.

Dear Helper,

Objective: to keep individual lists of words and learn to spell them.

Your child should be learning how to identify mis-spelled words and make lists of words to learn. Help them to find their spelling mistakes and add them to the list. Check that your child uses the **look, cover, write, check** method.

Full to -ful

The suffix **-ful** added to a noun, turns the noun into an adjective which usually means 'full of',

eg **beauty → beautiful** = 'full of beauty'.

Rules

-ful as a suffix has only one **l**, eg **hopeful**.
y changes to **i** when a suffix is added, eg **pitiful**.

- Complete the **adjective** column by adding **-ful** and changing **y to i** to the nouns if necessary.

Noun	Adjective
beauty	beautiful
care	
cheer	
deceit	
disgrace	
duty	
fancy	
grace	
hope	
mercy	
peace	
pity	
plenty	
spite	
success	

- Some words ending in **-ful** can be made opposite by changing **-ful** for **-less**, eg **careless**.

    Write down words from the above list which can be made opposite.
    Use the back of this sheet.

Dear Helper,

Objective: to explore spelling patterns: adding the suffix -ful.

Remind your child that a *suffix* is a group of letters added to the end of a word to change its meaning or use.
Check that your child takes care to apply the two rules, especially with the words ending in *-y*.

Dreadful language

English spelling is only partly phonetic. Many spellings are based on meaning, eg **electricity** is spelled to show its relationship with **electric**. Many spellings are historical, eg in the Middle Ages, every letter of **knight** was pronounced. English is the easiest European language to learn with the exception of spelling and pronunciation.

- Read and enjoy the poem.
- Highlight all the difficult spellings.

I take it you already know
Of tough and bough and cough and dough?
Others may stumble but not you
On hiccough, thorough, tough and through.
Well done! And now you wish perhaps
To learn the less familiar traps.

Beware of heard, a dreadful word,
That looks like beard and sounds like bird;
And dead, it's said like bed not bead –
For goodness' sake don't call it deed!
Watch out for meat and great and threat
(They rhyme with suite and straight and debt).

A moth is not a moth in mother,
Nor both in bother, broth in brother;
And here is not a match for there,
Nor dear and fear for bear and pear,
And then there's dose and rose and lose –
Just look at them – and goose and choose;

And cork and work and card and ward,
And font and front, and word and sword,
And do and go and thwart and cart –
A dreadful language? Man alive,
I'd mastered it when I was five.

- Find other spellings which use the same letter strings. Write them on the back of this sheet.

PHOTOCOPIABLE

Dear Helper,

Objective: to investigate words which have common letter sequencess but different pronunciations.
Read and discuss the explanation. Do you know any Europeans who have learned English? What did they find most difficult? Read and enjoy the poem, then investigate the letter sequences by finding matching words.

100 LITERACY HOMEWORK ACTIVITIES • YEAR 5 TERM 2

Homophone cards

aisle	currant	buoy	ate
faint	rain	night	their
gorilla	there	current	isle
program	principle	reign	feint
board	die	bored	guerilla
grate	stair	principal	programme
serial	coarse	dye	practice
weather	profit	stare	great
boy	eight	course	cereal
knight	practise	prophet	whether
flour	blew	blue	bear
great	bare	grate	flower

Set 1   **Set 2**

- Cut out the cards and play the game with a friend, parent or helper.
- Each player takes one set of cards. The first player puts down any card. The second player then has to find the matching **homophone** and define both homophones. If successful, that person wins a point.
- It is now the turn of the second player to put down a card and for the first person to find the matching homophone.

Dear Helper,

Objective: to distinguish between homophones (words with same pronunciation, but different spelling).
Supervise while your child plays the game with another child. Alternatively, join in yourself.

What do you do?

The suffix **-cian** means: someone who works with that subject.
Usually, the suffix -cian is added without any change to the root word. In some cases the word may already have a suffix which has to be removed. Just use common sense, as all the words are well-known.

- Look at these pictures of people doing their jobs.
  Write the appropriate **-cian** word underneath.

politics

diet

beauty

music

optics

physics

electricity

magic

mathematics

Dear Helper,

Objective: to recognise and spell the suffix -cian.

Remind your child that a *root* is the basic part of a word to which letters (a *suffix*) can be added to the ending to change its meaning or use. Your child may need help when adapting the *root* word to fit the *suffix* so that the resulting word is spelled correctly.

Name:

Technical tangle

✂

Let us cool the liquid further and watch it solidify at the same

mechanical power by the pistons, connecting rods and crankshafts of an engine.

To increase storage capacity, add a Zip drive. These take 100 megabyte

magnification as before. As we extract more heat the molecules

pronouns and verbs. Sometimes a ninth part of speech, articles, is added.

Heat energy made by the combustion of petrol and air is converted into

disks which are useful for storing large multimedia files. A scanner is also worth

moving ever more slowly, are pulled closer together, and the liquid contracts.

considering. Go for a 36-bit colour model with text-recognition software.

These are: adjectives, adverbs, conjunctions, interjections, nouns, prepositions,

Words are classified into eight parts of speech (sometimes called word classes).

The engine's efficiency depends on how much energy becomes useful power.

- The above lines of text are from four technical documents, but they have been muddled up. The documents are about **science, engineering, computers** and **language.** Use different colours to highlight which line of text belongs to which subject. Use a fifth colour to highlight technical terms.
- Cut out the lines of text and put the four different texts back together in the right order.

Dear Helper,

Objective: to search for, collect, define and spell technical words.
Your child may need help with the organisation of the task, which requires five different coloured pencils or highlighters, scissors and paste. Help your child to understand the technical terms which they find.

PHOTOCOPIABLE

Opposites attract

- Draw lines to link up the opposites. One has been done as an example.

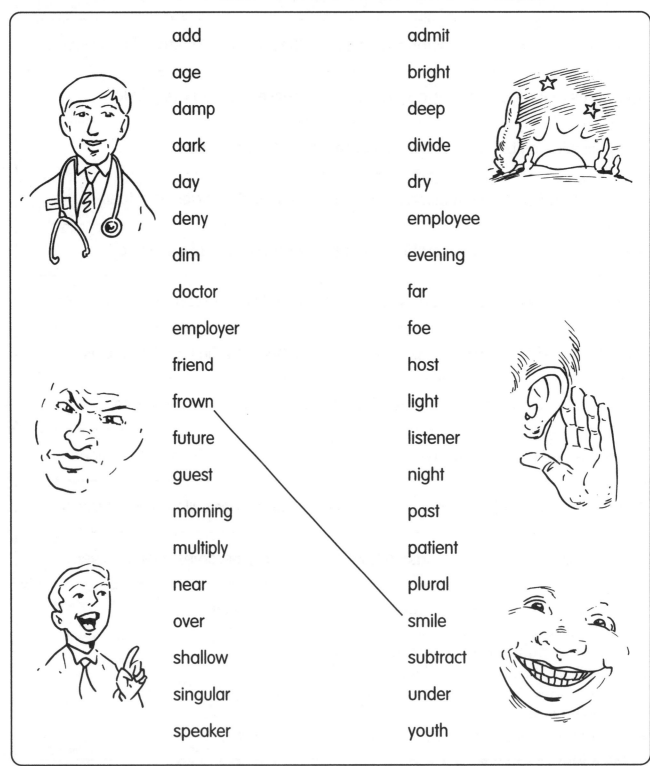

add	admit
age	bright
damp	deep
dark	divide
day	dry
deny	employee
dim	evening
doctor	far
employer	foe
friend	host
frown	light
future	listener
guest	night
morning	past
multiply	patient
near	plural
over	smile
shallow	subtract
singular	under
speaker	youth

Dear Helper,

Objective: to investigate opposites.
This is a straightforward exercise, but your child may need help to understand some of the words, eg 'foe', and to think of opposites for words like 'employer'.

Name:

Opposites by prefix

- Add the correct **prefix** to make the words below mean the opposite. The first one has been done as an example. Note that the spelling of the root word does not change when the prefix is added.
- Select from the following prefixes:

ab– , **dis–** , **il–** , **im–** , **in–** , **ir–** , **mis–** , **un–** .

dis	advantage		like
	approve		lock
	audible		moral
	aware		mortal
	behave		necessary
	comfortable		normal
	connect		obey
	convenient		order
	correct		perfect
	essential		pleasure
	fair		polite
	happy		possible
	human		regular
	kind		sane
	legal		visible
	legible		wise

Dear Helper,

Objective: to investigate opposites.

Remind your child that a *prefix* is a group of letters added to the beginning of a word to change its meaning . Read the words to your child. Check that they understand it, then ask: *What is its opposite?* The list of *prefixes* can then be used as prompts and aids to spelling.

Onomatopoeia

Some words suggest the sound they describe. This effect is called **onomatopoeia**. Here are some examples:

- Try to think of more examples and write them on the back of this sheet.
- **Onomatopoeic** words can be used together so that the sound of the paragraph or poem reflects its meaning. Read this onomatopoeic poem, then write your own, using words from the examples above. Use the back of this sheet or a separate piece of paper.

Plip, plop, rain drop
Drip, drop, drizzle.
Splatter, patter, plip, plop,
Miserable mist and mizzle.

Pitter, patter raindrops
Splash, plash, plonk, plink,
Dropping on my window panes
Like water dripping in a sink.

Dear Helper,

Objective: to explore onomatopoeia.

The term *onomatopoeia* (pronounced on-o-mah-ta-pee-a) is quite difficult to remember and spell, but the concept is easy – and fun. Take it in turns to say the words in a way which emphasises their sound. Talk about creatures, places and situations where each word might be used. Help your child to develop one of the ideas into a poem.

Don't take it literally

- Study this table which explains the terms **literal**, **figurative**, **metaphor** and **simile**.
- Add your own examples to the table.

Literal Straightforward, factual way of saying something	**Figurative** An imaginative way of saying something, often by comparing one thing to another.	
	Simile A comparison using 'like' or 'as'.	**Metaphor** A direct comparison, saying one thing is another.
My feet are cold. Ordinary post is slow. He is tall.	My feet are like ice. Ordinary post is as slow as a snail. He is as tall as a giant.	My feet are ice. Original post is snail mail. He is a giant of a man.
Own examples		

Dear Helper,

Objective: to investigate language that creates images in the reader's mind.

Understanding how language can be used to heighten description will help your child apprieciate it in reading and, hopefully, apply it to their writing. Take the time to go over the explanation in the table, adding your own examples.

Table-top planet

- Read this literal–figurative poem. Notice how all the phrases and sentences on the left-hand side are **literal** and all those on the right are **figurative**. The figurative statements are mostly metaphors, but there is one simile – can you find it?

Literal	**Figurative**
My pen is	a minature space ship full of tiny aliens.
The top of the table is	a flat brown field on which the spaceship has landed.
This piece of paper is	a patch of cold, fresh snow.
My eraser is	the aliens' exploration vehicle.
These tiny bits left by the eraser are	the aliens exploring in their spacesuits.
The little bits are clustered round the pen.	They want to go back home to Venus where it is as hot as a pressure cooker.
The pen is empty.	But they have run out of fuel.
I'm going to throw the pen away and clean my desk.	A giant earthling wipes them out.

- Write your own literal–figurative poem. Start with a group of everyday objects (eg the contents of your pocket or schoolbag or the dining table) and let your imagination create a new world around them.

Dear Helper,

Objective: to investigate and create metaphors.
Although your child will have been taught the terms, remind them what *literal* (realistic, factual) and *figurative* (imaginative, symbolic) mean. Read the poem with your child, taking half-lines each. Talk about how ordinary things are transformed by imagination.

Name:

Sickly soup

- Take two simple sentences and try re-ordering them in different ways, as shown below.

Two simple sentences	Effect of the changes
The witch offered Amy some soup. Amy felt sick.	These could be two unrelated sentences. Amy might have felt sick for any reason.
Re-ordered	
The witch offered Amy some soup and she felt sick.	**The two sentences are joined into one. 'Amy' from the second sentence is changed to the pronoun 'she' to avoid repetition.**
When the witch offered Amy some soup, she felt sick.	**The word 'when' emphasises that it was the offer of soup that made Amy feel sick.**
Amy felt sick because the witch offered her some soup.	**As above, but switching the clauses, places the emphasis on Amy rather than the witch.**

- Experiment with the following simple sentences in the same way as the example above.

Tim ran as fast as he could. Tim missed the bus.

Tara flicked through all 30 channels. There was nothing worth watching.

It was dark. The numerals on the clock glowed faintly.

Sam failed the test. He did not revise.

It rained. They got wet.

Dear Helper,

Objective: to re-order and combine simple sentences.

It is important for the children to understand how sentences can be re-ordered and combined. Help your child to re-order the simple sentences above. If they get stuck, suggest using conjunctions (joining words) such as: *although, and, as, because, but, for, until, when, where, while.*

Are we agreed?

Singular subjects require singular verbs: eg **the dog barks.**
Plural subjects take plural verbs: eg **the dogs bark.**
When this is done correctly, the subject (the noun or noun phrase) and verb (action word) are said to **agree**.

Tip: Think hard about whether the subject of the sentence is **singular** (one) or **plural** (more than one), eg **a box of tools** is singular, because it is the **box** that is the subject, not the tools.

- Underline the correct verb in each of these sentences.

The children (look/looks) tired.

This letter from the headteacher (explain/explains) the new school rules.

The exhibition of children's writing (is/are) in the hall.

The exhibition of children's art and pottery (is/are) in the foyer.

One of the computers (has/have) been sent back to be repaired.

The distress rockets fired from the *Titanic* (was/were) seen by the *Californian's* officer on watch.

The price of the CDs (was/were) too high.

This box of chocolates (was/were) a gift.

Carelessness in the use of tools (cause/causes) most of the accidents in Design Technology lessons.

Tim, as well as Tom, Judy and Trudy, (has/have) decided to join the choir.

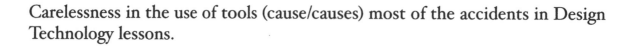

Dear Helper,

Objective: to ensure agreement between nouns and verbs.

Agreement in language is about how words and phrases are used together consistently. Most of us can hear whether something 'sounds' right or wrong. So, encourage your child to say the words aloud when reading and writing. Difficulties may arise with subjects which are singular, but sound as if they are plural, eg a *box of chocolates* (the subject is *box* which is singular, not *chocolates* which is plural).

Name:

Video audiences

- Adapt this text from an encyclopaedia for young adults by:
  - removing as many technical terms as possible from the text and the diagram, eg **iron oxide, bandwidth**;
  - simplifying any other difficult vocabulary, eg **generate, phased**;
  - shortening sentences, where possible, eg the second sentence can be divided into two.

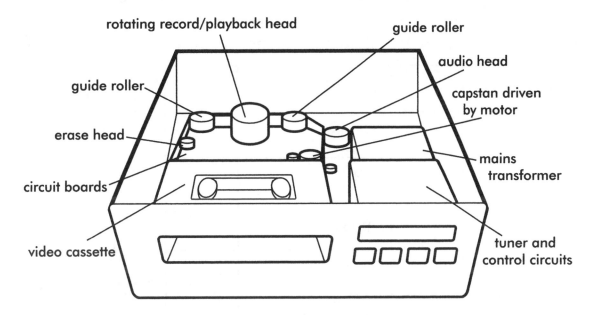

A video recorder stores television signals as patterns of magnetised iron oxide on magnetic tape. When the recorded tape is played back, the magnetised patterns generate an electrical signal which can be viewed on a television.

Television signals cannot be recorded on an ordinary cassette recorder because television signals have a bandwidth of about 6 MHz and need a much higher scanning speed to fit them onto tape. For this reason, a video cassette recorder (VCR) uses wider tape and runs at a higher speed than an audio cassette recorder.

Most home video recorders use a system called 'helical scan'. In this system a record/play head is placed on a revolving drum. The tape is wrapped around the drum at an angle between 90° and 360°. In the early 1980s, there were two competing formats: Betamax and VHS. VHS became the most popular and Betamax was phased out.

Today, VCRs are facing competition from a new medium: DVD – the Digital Versatile Disk. This gives better quality and is more compact, though at the moment, it cannot record. However, DVD players which can also record are sure to follow soon, and today's familiar VCRs will be obsolete.

Dear Helper,

Objective: to adapt writing for different audiences.
Your child may need help with simplifying difficult vocabulary, either by leaving it out altogether or by putting it in simple terms. Let your child use a dictionary if necessary.

Proper or common?

A **proper noun** names a specific person, place, time, occasion or thing. Proper nouns begin with capital letters. They usually have no plurals.

A **common noun** names a class of things. Common nouns have determiners ('a', 'the', 'some') and have plural forms (eg by adding **s**).

- Someone has sorted these nouns into the two columns, **proper nouns** and **common nouns**. Have they done it correctly? Give a ✓ for correct and a ✗ for wrong answer. Write an encouraging comment for them at the bottom.

Proper nouns	✓ or ✗	Common nouns	✓ or ✗
accordion		John Keats	
book		London	
magazine		girl	
budgie		mouse	
Canada		Mrs Trubb	
dinosaur		Humber Bridge	
Doctor Johnson		Niagara Falls	
Easter		ocean	
France		Ted	
gorilla		Titanic	
Tuesday		mushroom	
internet		Whitney Avenue	

Comment _____

Dear Helper,

Objective: to revise different kinds of noun.
Read through the list of nouns and ask your child whether they are names of specific people, places, times, occasions or things. If so, they are proper nouns. Help your child to think of other nouns to go in each column.

Trudy's Dream Present

Pronouns are used in place of nouns to avoid repetition.
Personal pronouns: I, you, he, she, it, me, him, her, my, mine,
your, yours, his, hers, its, we, they, us, them, our, ours, their, theirs.

- Read Version 1 of *Trudy's Dream Present*, an
  example of a writer not using any personal pronouns.

Version 1

Trudy got Trudy's dream present for Christmas – a mobile phone. Trudy couldn't wait
to try the mobile phone out, so Trudy dialled a number. Trudy was disappointed when
nothing happened. Then Trudy realised that Trudy hadn't turned the mobile phone
on. Trudy flicked the switch and tried again, but again Trudy was disappointed
because the mobile phone was still dead. Just then, Trudy's friend, Trisha, came into
the room. Trudy told Trisha that Trudy had got a mobile phone for Christmas. 'Great,
so has Trisha!' said Trisha. 'Trudy and Trisha can call each other!' Trudy said that Trudy
had tried but the mobile phone wouldn't work. Trisha asked if Trisha could have a
look. Trisha looked at the battery indicator. 'Trisha thought so,' said Trisha. 'Trudy
hasn't charged the battery!'

- Now read Version 2 of *Trudy's Dream Present*, an
  example of a writer using too many personal pronouns.

Version 2

She got her dream present for Christmas – a mobile phone. She couldn't wait to try it
out, so she dialled a number. She was disappointed when nothing happened. Then she
realised that she hadn't turned it on. She flicked the switch and tried again, but again
she was disappointed because the phone was still dead. Just then, her friend came into
the room. She told her that she had got a mobile phone for Christmas. 'Great, so
have I,' she said. 'We can call each other!' She said that she had tried but it wouldn't
work. She asked if she could have a look. She looked at the battery indicator. 'I
thought so,' said she. 'You haven't charged the battery!'

- Write your own version of *Trudy's Dream Present* with the right balance of
  personal pronouns and names. Use the back of this sheet or a separate
  piece of paper.

Dear Helper,

Objective: to revise the function of pronouns.
Read through the texts with your child. Help them to make the corrections orally by using simple common sense
– eg what sounds right. If necessary, help with producing the written version.

PHOTOCOPIABLE

100 LITERACY HOMEWORK ACTIVITIES • YEAR 5 TERM 2

Caribbean folk tale

Spoken language features:

- incomplete sentences
- importance of tone of voice
- use of gesture, facial expression, etc.
- simple plot structure
- informal style, perhaps with dialect

Written language features:

- carefully constructed sentences
- punctuation to help the reader
- more detail in descriptions
- more complex plot structure
- more formal style

- Find and underline examples of the characteristics of **spoken** language in this Caribbean folk tale.

Oral version of a Caribbean folk tale

Let me tell 'ee the story of Rose Hall – that was one big house! – the best in Jamaica, folks say. Well, it was owned by John Palmer – he be one of them colonial planters – worth a fortune a was and all from the hard work of black brothers and sisters. (*Sadly*) Slaves, they was. Well. His troubles began when he brought a bride back to Rose Hall – that was 1820, I mind. At first they was happy enough, but Annie, well a was only 18, and she soon got tired o' that lardy husband – well, he was old man, do yo see, and she was young girl – so she takes up wi' a young man – a slave, he was. When her husband find out, he go stark staring mad and they had real bad argument. (*Frowns*.). Soon after, John Palmer, he was found dead. Well, they blame Annie. They say that she got her lover to strangle him. Soon after that she had the slave whip to death so as to get rid of the only witness. Well, Annie was master now – and a cruel one! (*Gestures as if using a rod*.) She rule the estate with a rod of iron – ooh and was she bad to her slaves! One day she whip a slave so bad that his back was ripped open 'til yo could see the bone! (*Shakes head*.) That boy was so wild wi' pain he broke loose and tried to strangle her. Ha, ha – the best part is that when she cry for help, the other slaves, they help him – not her! They put a mattress on her and jump on it until she was suffocated to death – serve her right too! (*Grins and nods*.) They say she haunt the place now. (*Frowns*.). Well, guess what – that old place – Rose Hall – was a ruin for years, but now they've done it all up – the Jamaican government – for tourists – ha ha – but yo wouldn't catch me goin' there (*waves hand*) – no, no, not with the ghost of old Annie and all!

Extension

- Change the oral story into a written story. Use a separate sheet of paper.

Dear Helper,

Objective: to be aware of the differences between spoken and written language.

This activity should help your child understand how meaning is conveyed in spoken language through context, tone of voice, facial expression and gesture. In written language, all this has to be conveyed through word choice, sentence construction and punctuation. Read the story to your child, trying to make it as authentically 'oral' as possible. Alternatively, tell your child an oral story of your own and then ask: *How would it be different if it were written in a book?*

Combine sentences

- Combine these sentences by writing the appropriate **conjunctions** in the empty box. Look for more than one possible conjunction.

  Conjunctions: although, and, as, because, but, for, until, when, where, while

The girls were frightened		they heard the thunder.
They got soaked		it rained unexpectedly.
They decided to take shelter		the rain stopped.
Tara felt uneasy		they entered the old house.
Zara tried to switch on the lights		there was no electricity.
Tara opened a cupboard		she found a skeleton.
She was about to scream		Zara pointed out that it was plastic.
The girls tried to sleep		they were too nervous.
Zara woke up early		a cock crowed loudly.
Tara was happy		the rain had stopped.

Extension

- Use the sentences to write a story. Make them more interesting by combining them and adding more detail. You can use the back of the sheet or a separate piece of paper.

Dear Helper,

Objective: to construct sentences by combining two shorter sentences.

Read these sentences with your child, taking a column each and trying out different conjunctions orally. Your child will then find it easy to write in appropriate conjunctions.

Name:

Phantom phrases

- Fill each gap in the passage below with one of the following phrases or clauses. Add a comma before and after the phrase or clause (unless it comes at the end of a sentence).

> a horrifying creature in a white mask

> who was a young chorus girl

> in a trembling voice

> little knowing the price she would pay

> if you co-operate with me

> on the opening night of the new production

> turning white as a sheet

> no matter what other work she had to do

> running backwards and forwards in a panic

> which was a huge building with a lake far underneath

The Paris Opera House _____ was said to be

haunted. The ghost _____ had once been a

famous tenor. One day Christine _____ was

sitting alone in her dressing room when she heard a strange voice.

'Christine', whispered the voice, 'I can make you famous _____

_____,'

'Why do you want to?' answered Christine _____

_____.

'Revenge on Carlotta!' replied the phantom.

From that day onwards _____ the

phantom made Christine practise for at least three hours _____

_____

Then _____ Carlotta received a

threatening note from the phantom. She read it and

_____ fainted.

Quick!' shouted the manager _____

'find Christine. Tell her to put on Carlotta's dress and go on stage!'

So Christine got her chance at last.

Dear Helper,

Objective: to use commas when adding phrases and clauses to sentences.
Your child should be learning how punctuation helps the reader make sense of complex sentences. This will help their reading and writing. Read the story with your child and discuss which phrases fit in which gap. Check that they have used a comma before and after each clause or phrase.

100 LITERACY HOMEWORK ACTIVITIES • YEAR 5 TERM 2

Mercury and the Forester

- This is a fable (by Aesop). Read it, and then write a few points about how it is different from an ordinary story.

A forester was felling a tree on the bank of a river, when his axe slipped out of his hands and fell into the water. As he stood by the water grumbling about his lost axe, the god Mercury appeared and asked him why he was upset.

When the forester told him, Mercury dived into the river. He came up with a golden axe and asked him if it was the one he had lost. The forester replied that it was not, and Mercury dived a second time. This time he came up with a silver axe.

'No, that is not mine either,' said the forester.

Once again Mercury dived into the river, and this time came up with the missing axe. The forester was delighted at having his axe returned, and thanked Mercury warmly. Mercury was so pleased with his honesty that he gave him the other two axes as a reward.

When the forester told the story to his friends, one of them was filled with envy and decided to try his luck in the same way. So he went to fell a tree at the edge of the river, and pretended to drop his axe into the water. Mercury appeared as before and offered to find the lost axe. He dived in and came up with a golden axe just as he had done before. Without waiting to be asked whether it was his or not, the man cried, 'That's mine, that's mine!' and tried to grab the precious object. But Mercury was so disgusted at his dishonesty that he refused to give him the golden axe, and also refused to find the one he had lost.

Moral: Honesty is the best policy.

Notes on differences:

Extension

- Write your own fable which ends with the same moral. Use the back of this sheet.

Dear Helper,

Objective: to identify the features of fables.
Share the reading of this fable with your child. Then, discuss how it is different from an ordinary story. Ask: *What is the last line of the story?*

The Mistletoe Bough

• Read the poem, then tell the story to your helper.

The mistletoe hung in the castle hall,
The holly branch shone on the old oak wall;
And the baron's retainers[1] were happy that day,
Keeping their Christmas holiday.
The baron saw with a father's pride
His beautiful child, young Lovell's bride;
While she with her bright eyes seemed to be
The star of the goodly company.

'I'm weary of dancing now,' she cried;
'Here wait a moment – I'll hide – I'll hide!
And, Lovell, be sure you are first to trace
The clue to my secret hiding place.'
Away she ran – and her friends began
Each tower to search, and each nook to scan;
And young Lovell cried, 'Oh where do you hide?
I'm lonely without you, my own dear bride.'

They search all night and they searched next day!
And they kept on searching 'til a week passed away!
In the highest, the lowest, the loneliest spot,
Young Lovell sought wildly – but found her not.
And years flew by, and their grief at last
Was told as a sorrowful tale long past,
And when Lovell appeared, the children cried,
'See! the old man weeps for his long lost bride.'

At length an oak chest, that had long lain hid,
Was found in the castle. They raised the lid –
And a skeleton form lay mouldering[2] there,
In the bridal wreath of that lady fair!
Oh! sad was her fate! – in playful jest
She hid from her lord in the old oak chest.
It closed with a click – and, dreadful doom,
The bride lay locked in her living tomb!

Thomas Haynes Bayley (slightly adapted)

[1]*retainers = servants and followers;* [2]*mouldering = rotting*

Dear Helper,

Objective: to read a narrative poem and show understanding of the story.

Share the reading of the poem with your child, eg taking verses in turn. Then help your child to retell the story in the poem. Discuss what happened and talk about similar incidents today, eg children who get caught in abandoned fridges.

Name:

Overheard on a Saltmarsh

● Read this poem aloud, then plan a performance of it.

Nymph, nymph, what are your beads?
Green glass, goblin. Why do you stare at them?
Give them me.
       No.
Give them me. Give them me.
       No.
Then I will howl all night in the reeds,
Lie in the mud and howl for them.
Goblin, why do you love them so?
They are better than stars or water,
Better than voices of winds that sing,
Better than any man's fair daughter,
Your green glass beads on a silver ring.
Hush I stole them out of the moon.
Give me your beads, I desire them.
       No.
I will howl in a deep lagoon
For your green glass beads, I love them so.
Give them me. Give them.
       No.

Harold Monro

Dear Helper,

Objective: to read and plan to perform a poem.
Read the poem with your child and talk about how it involves two characters who have a dialogue. Help your child to plan a performance. This could include simple movements, eg crouching to suggest a goblin. Encourage your child to use a realistic tone of voice.

PHOTOCOPIABLE

All kinds of poems

Definitions

A **clerihew** is a four-line comic poem about a person who is named in the first line.
A **haiku** consists of seventeen syllables.
A **limerick** is a short humorous poem with a bouncy rhythm.
A **sonnet** has rhyme and fourteen lines.
Many **ballads** have rhyme schemes of a b c b.

- Read these poems or parts of poems aloud.
- Write down the name of the form used in each poem.
  Use the above definitions to help you.
- Try to add more information to the definitions. Use the back of this sheet.

I sat next to a duchess at tea,
Distressed as a person could be.
Her rumblings abdominal
Were simply phenomenal
And everyone thought it was me.
Anon

Form_____

The King sits in Dumfermlin town
Drinking the blood-red wine:
'O, where will I get a skilly skipper
To sail this ship of mine?'
Anon

Form_____

Sir Francis Drake
Learned to sail on a lake –
But defeating the Armada
Was much harder!
Anon

Form_____

Earth has not anything to show more fair:
Dull would he be of soul who could pass by
A sight so touching in its majesty:
This City now doth, like a garment, wear
The beauty of the morning; silent, bare,
Ships, towers, domes, theatres, and temples lie
Open unto the fields, and to the sky;
All bright and glittering in the smokeless air.
Never did sun more beautifully steep
In his first splendour, valley, rock, or hill;
Ne'er saw I, never felt, a calm so deep!
The river glideth at his own sweet will:
Dear God! the very houses seem asleep;
And all that mighty heart is lying still!
William Wordsworth

Form_____

Storm clouds gathering
The forest sighs in the wind
A screech from a crow.
Piatto

Form_____

Dear Helper,

Objective: to understand terms which describe different kinds of poem.

Share the reading of these poems with your child, then help them to match each one to the definitions given above.

Arthur: chosen king

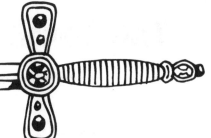

- Read this famous passage from the legend of King Arthur.
- Write your version of the episode. You can use the back of the sheet or a separate piece of paper.

On Christmas Eve, Bishop Brice spoke to the nobles of Britain in the great church at Winchester. When the service ended, a miraculous stone was found outside the church. In the stone was firmly fixed a sword, with the following words engraved on its hilt:

'I am the sword Excalibur,
A sword only a king can draw.'

Bishop Brice, gave thanks to God and ordered that whoever could draw out the sword from the stone, should be acknowledged as the rightful king of the Britons. The most famous knights, one after another, tried their strength, but the miraculous sword would not be moved. It stayed there until Candlemas, until Easter, and until Pentecost, when the best knights in the kingdom assembled for the annual tournament.

Arthur, who was at that time serving as a squire to Sir Kay, came with him to the tournament that year. Sir Kay fought with great success in the tournament, but unluckily broke his sword in one of the bouts. He sent Arthur for a new one. Arthur hurried home, but saw the sword in the stone, and decided to save himself a long journey. He drew the sword out quite easily and took it to his master.

When Sir Kay saw the sword, he recognised it by the engraving on its hilt and asked Arthur how he got it. 'I just pulled it out,' said Arthur. Sir Kay, still doubting, took Arthur to the stone, and thrust the sword back in to see if he could pull it out again. By this time, a large crowd had gathered. First, Sir Kay tried to pull it out himself, but though he heaved with all his might, it would not give an inch. Then he asked Arthur to try. Arthur stepped up to the stone and pulled out the sword as smoothly as from a well-greased scabbard.

Sir Kay, and all present, kneeled before him and proclaimed him king.

Dear Helper,

Objective: to write a version of a known legend.
Share the reading of this passage with your child. Then, talk about the many different ways in which the story has been retold. Help your child to decide on a way of retelling the story.

PHOTOCOPIABLE

The Lambton worm

- Read this 'choice' story. Experiment with different choices.

1 Long ago, in the Middle Ages, at a place called Lambton, a young man caught a strange worm when he was fishing. The worm was like nothing he had ever seen before. It had scales, four tiny legs, and a mouthful of sharp teeth.

If you think he should throw it back, go to 2. If you think he should kill it, go to 3.

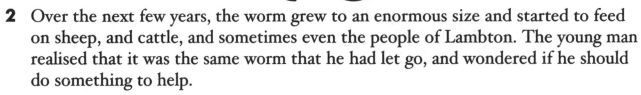

2 Over the next few years, the worm grew to an enormous size and started to feed on sheep, and cattle, and sometimes even the people of Lambton. The young man realised that it was the same worm that he had let go, and wondered if he should do something to help.

If you think he should try to kill it, go to 3. If you think he should keep quiet, go to 4.

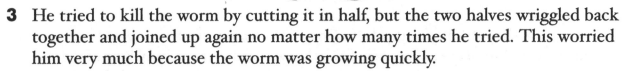

3 He tried to kill the worm by cutting it in half, but the two halves wriggled back together and joined up again no matter how many times he tried. This worried him very much because the worm was growing quickly.

If you think he should give up, go to 4. If you think he should seek the help of the wise woman, go to 5.

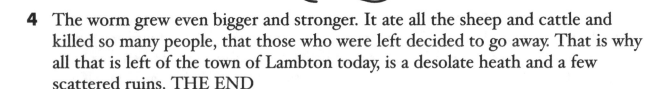

4 The worm grew even bigger and stronger. It ate all the sheep and cattle and killed so many people, that those who were left decided to go away. That is why all that is left of the town of Lambton today, is a desolate heath and a few scattered ruins. THE END

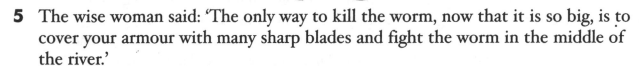

5 The wise woman said: 'The only way to kill the worm, now that it is so big, is to cover your armour with many sharp blades and fight the worm in the middle of the river.'

If you think that is bad advice, go to 4. If you think it is worth a try, go to 6.

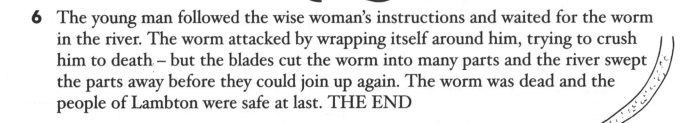

6 The young man followed the wise woman's instructions and waited for the worm in the river. The worm attacked by wrapping itself around him, trying to crush him to death – but the blades cut the worm into many parts and the river swept the parts away before they could join up again. The worm was dead and the people of Lambton were safe at last. THE END

Dear Helper,

Objective: to write a version of a legend.
Read each section with your child. Discuss and experiment with the choices given. Which choices did your child think made for the best story? Encourage and help your child to retell another legend as a 'choice' story.

Write on

- This is part of a longer narrative poem, 'King John and the Abbot of Canterbury'. Read the poem, then continue it in your own way. Use a separate sheet.

An ancient story I'll tell you anon
Of a notable prince that was called King John;
And he ruled England with main[1] and with might,
For he did great wrong, and maintained little right.

And I'll tell you a story, a story so merrie,
Concerning the Abbot of Canterbury;
How for his housekeeping and high renown,[2]
They rode post[3] for him to fair London town.

An hundred men, the king did hear say,
The abbot kept in his house every day;
And fifty gold chains without any doubt,
In velvet coats waited the abbot about.

'How now, father abbot, I hear of thee,
Thou keepest a far better house than me;
And for thy housekeeping and high renown,
I fear thou work'st treason against my crown.'

'My liege,'[4] quo[5] the abbot, 'I would it were known
I never spend nothing, but what is my own;
And I trust your grace will do me no deere,[6]
For spending of my own true-gotten gear.'

'Yes, yes. Father abbot, thy fault is high,
And now for the same thou needst must die;
For except[7] thou canst answer me questions three,
The head shall be smitten[8] from thy bodie.

'And first,' quo' the king, 'when I'm in this stead,[9]
With my crown of gold so fair on my head,
Among all my liege-men so noble of birth,
Thou must tell me to one penny what I am worth.

'Secondlie, tell me, without any doubt,
How soon I may ride the whole world about;
And at the third question thou must not shrink,
But tell me here truly what I do think.'

Anon.

[1]*main = force;* [2]*housekeeping and high renown = wealth and fame;* [3]*rode post = travelled;*
[4]*liege = lord/master;* [5]*quo' = said;* [6]*deere = harm;* [7]*For except = unless;* [8]*smitten = cut off;* [9]*stead = way.*

- Do you think the abbot was able to save his life by answering the three questions?
- Write about what you think happened. If you can, write in verses of rhyming couplets.

Dear Helper,

Objective: to write additional verses for a poem.

Share the reading of the poem with your child, taking verses in turn. Discuss the story and identify the three questions the king asks the abbot. Ask: *How might the abbot have answered the king?* Encourage your child to hear the rhythm of the poem and, if possible, to use the rhythm and rhyme scheme when writing extra verses.

PHOTOCOPIABLE

Science fiction cards: plots

Plot
Intergalactic Titanic

A luxury space liner hits a 'spaceberg' (piece of ice left by a comet).

Plot
Killing Time

The hero(ine) must travel back in time to stop an evil person from being born.

Plot
Big Bang

Earth is threatened by a giant asteroid.

Plot
Piggy-in-the-Middle

Earth gets caught in the middle of a war between two galactic civilisations.

Plot
Death is Dead

Death is cured. Overpopulation threatens the earth.

Plot
Pentium 1000

A super-powerful computer system decides to take over the universe.

Plot
Virtual Unreality

After a computer whizz-kid invents a totally realistic virtual reality program, nobody can tell what is real and what is not.

Plot
Beauty and the Beast

A multi-limbed, bug-eyed alien falls in love with an earth girl.

Science Fiction Cards: Plots

- Cut out these cards. Shuffle them and turn them face down. Choose one and make up a story to fit the chosen plot. Prepare to tell the story to the class.

Dear Helper,

Objective: to prepare for oral story-telling.
Play the oral story-telling game with your child, then help them polish one of the stories for presentation to the class.

PHOTOCOPIABLE

Name:

Science fiction cards: endings

Ending
I, Robot

The hero of the story takes off his skin and reveals that he is a robot.

Ending
Just a Game

We find out that the story was just a computer game played by children.

Ending
Adam and Eve

The hero and heroine escape to a new planet that is the uninhabited third planet of a yellow star.

Ending
Future Planet

Space explorers find out that they are not on another planet, but the earth of the far future.

Ending
Achilles' Heel

Alien invaders are technically superior, but we beat them by finding a weak spot.

Ending
Time Warp

Time travellers return to their own time to find out that everything has changed.

Ending
Whizzkid Burnout

A teenage whizz kid makes a great new discovery, but when he turns 20, he loses his genius.

Ending
In Disguise

The ruler of the galaxy turns out to be your best friend/dog/next door neighbour in disguise to avoid assassination.

Science Fiction Cards:
Endings

SCIENCE FICTION CARDS

- Cut out these cards. Shuffle them and turn them face down. Choose one and make up a story to fit the chosen ending. Prepare to tell the story to the class.

Dear Helper,

Objective: to prepare for oral story-telling.

Play the oral story-telling game with your child, then help them polish one of the stories for presentation to the class.

Colour television

- Read this explanatory text and highlight examples of **impersonal style, complex sentences, passive voice, technical vocabulary, explanatory diagrams.**

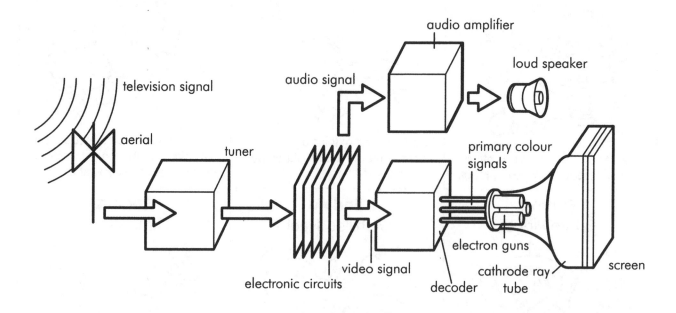

Colour television broadcasting began in the United States in 1954 using the NTSC (National Television Systems Committee) system. Great Britain and West Germany introduced colour in 1967 using the PAL (Phase Alternation Line) system. In the same year, France and the Soviet Union introduced SECAM (systeme electronique couleur avec memoire).

A **television signal** starts with a television camera which uses a device called an image orthicon tube. This tube turns light waves into electrical signals. The signals are broadcast by a transmitter using Ultra High Frequency radio waves.

These signals are received by an **aerial** (note that cable and satellite systems are beginning to replace aerials). The **aerial** takes the radio waves to a **tuner** which turns the waves into electrical signals similar to those made by the television camera. **Electronic circuits** split the signal into an **audio signal** and a **video signal.** The audio signals are sent to an **audio amplifier** and then to a **loudspeaker**. The video signals are sent to a **decoder** which separates the **primary colour signals**. They are then sent to **electron guns** which fire them down the **cathode ray tube** to the screen.

Dear Helper,

Objective: to read an explanatory text.

Help your child by providing a set of coloured pencils or highlighters and helping them to understand and find examples of the following: *impersonal style, complex sentences, passive voice, technical vocabulary, explanatory diagrams.*

Name:

Concept mapping

- Look at this **concept map** for **Dinosaurs.** See how the concept map flows outward from known facts to questions.
- Draw your own concept map for a topic you wish to research in the space below.

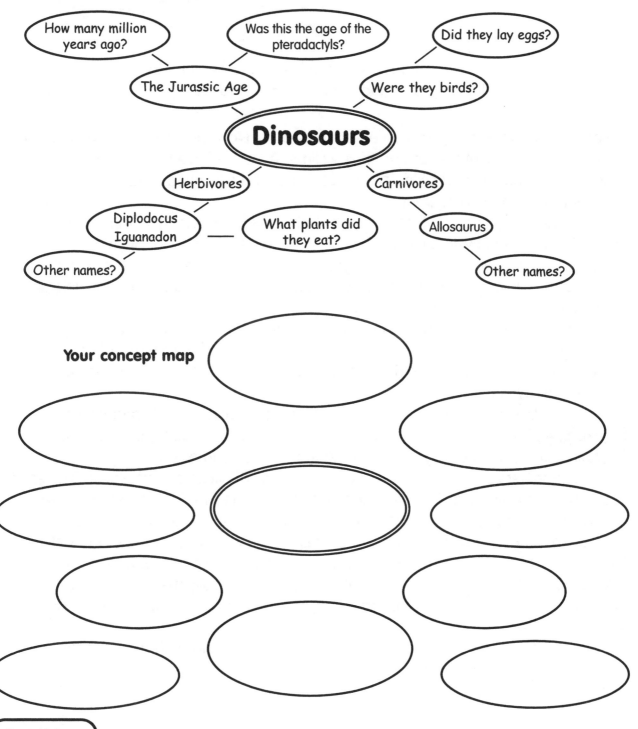

Dear Helper,

Objective: to find out what you know, need or want to know about a topic.

Making a concept map helps children to clarify what they want to research. Help your child to choose a topic to write in the central oval, ensuring that it is something they know about. Then, help to brainstorm ideas and questions for the topic.

Scanning

- Scan the text below to find information about:
  - bullies;
  - victims;
  - the methods of the researchers.

- Use three different coloured pens to highlight the different information.
- Time how long it took you to find the information about each topic.

Recent research into bullying, carried out by staff at Northcliffe College, has helped us to find out more about bullies and their victims. A team of five researchers visited 20 schools. They interviewed children and teachers, and observed children in the classroom and in the playground.

The research showed that 60% of bullies were boys and 40% were girls. Boy bullies tend to use physical forms of bullying, for example, hitting, pushing and stealing from their victims. The report gives some upsetting examples: one boy had his head pushed down a toilet, another had his schoolbag kicked around the field like a football, and a third had his lunch money taken from him.

Girl bullies are more likely to use name-calling and 'sending to Coventry' (not speaking to the victim). At one school, a pupil who worked hard was called 'swot' until she burst into tears. Another girl said that nobody would talk to her or play with her because she was fat.

The victims of bullying are often chosen for a weakness. This might be physical, for example, being small, having a stammer, wearing spectacles, or some other characteristic such as being new, or appearing to be timid or nervous.

Researchers interviewed over 100 bullies and 100 victims, and placed the results in a computer database. This allowed them to examine the data in many different ways, often enabling them to come up with new information about the problem.

For example, they found out that bullies like easy victims. Some of the victims interviewed tried to fight back. For example, one girl, whose books were thrown in the bin, threw her bully's books in the bin the next day. The bully then got her friends to gang up on her. Yet, by the following week, she left her alone and started to pick on somebody else.

At the end of their report, the researchers recommended that every school should have an effective policy to prevent bullying and listed ten points that every bullying policy should include.

Dear Helper,

Objective: to locate information confidently and efficiently through scanning.
Help your child by acting as time-keeper for this activity.

Internet download

Imagine your teacher has asked for some information about horses and you have found the following information on the internet.

www.horseshomepage.com

The HORSE (*Equus caballus*) is an ungulate mammal of the family *Equidae*. The evolution of the horse commenced in the Eocene era with an animal the size of a dog called Dawn Horse (*Eohippus*). Eohippus is believed to have originated in Asia or Africa. As the horse grew in size, it was widely domesticated and used by man as a beast of burden.

As the horse evolved, the teeth became adapted to cropping grass, and the feet became adapted for speedy running. Eohippus had four toes, but one of these developed to become the hoof, while the others dwindled to small digits called 'splints'.

The family Equidae also includes the zebra and the ass. One interesting member of the family was the quagga, which, in appearance, was half zebra, half horse. The quagga recently became extinct.

A young male horse is called a 'colt'; a female horse is called a 'filly'; an adult male is called a 'stallion', and an adult female a 'mare'. Despite metrication, horses are still measured in a unit called a 'hand' which is approximately 10 cm.

- Put this information into your own words by:
  - removing or changing all words that you would not normally use yourself, eg Latin terms – keep only essential technical terms such as 'stallion';
  - shortening sentences where necessary;
  - simplifying punctuation so that it is similar to what you would use yourself. You could begin like this:

    ### The horse is a hoofed mammal. Its evolution began...

Dear Helper,

Objective: to understand what is meant by 'in your own words'.
Your child will often wish to use information from books, CD ROMs and the internet. This task will help your child to do this properly by adapting rather than copying the text. Help your child to understand the text, using a dictionary where necessary.

Non–fiction redrafting checklist

- Use this checklist to evaluate a piece of your non-fiction writing.

Part 1: Content and Presentation

✓   Does the text use the conventions of the chosen genre?

✓   **Recounts**   should be written in chronological order and organised in paragraphs and chapters.

✓   **Instructions**   should be clear. The clearest instructions are set out step-by-step and are often helped by numbered or bulleted points and diagrams.

✓   **Reports**   should contain precise information including facts and figures. Subheadings, tables and graphs can be very helpful.

✓   **Explanations**   should be clear and are usually written in paragraphs. Block paragraphs may be used. Pictures or diagrams will help to make the explanations clearer.

✓   **Persuasive texts**   should begin with an explanation of the issue followed by a series of arguments. Advertisements and leaflets should also have illustrations to add to their impact.

Part 2: Grammar, Punctuation and Spelling

✓   Has the correct tense been used for verbs (eg recounts should be written in the past tense, instructions should use the imperative mood, explanations and persuasive texts are usually in the present tense)?

✓   Have capital letters, commas, full stops, question marks and exclamation marks been used in the right places?

✓   Has other helpful punctuation been used where appropriate (eg bullet points, colons and semi-colons in complex lists etc)?

✓   Check spelling.

Dear Helper,

Objective: to evaluate own work.

Help your child to use this checklist to check through and evaluate a piece of their non-fiction writing.

Look, cover, write, check (3)

- **Look** at each word in the first column, **cover** it up, **write** it in the second column, **check** it, then place a ✓ (correct) or a ✗ (wrong) after it.

Look	Write	Check	Look	Write	Check
neighbour			rhyme		
noticeable			rhythm		
occasionally			seize		
occur			separate		
once			separately		
panicked			similar		
parallel			sincerely		
patient			solemn		
possess			success		
priest			surprise		
professor			thorough		
pursue			twelfth		
queue			unnecessary		
queueing			vicious		
receive			weight		
recommend			whistle		
remember			yacht		
restaurant			yield		

- Add to the list words from your own writing that you need to learn.

Dear Helper,

Objective: to keep individual lists of words and learn to spell them.

Your child should be learning how to identify mis-spelled words and make lists of words to learn. Help them to find their spelling mistakes and add them to the list. Check that your child uses the **look, cover, write, check** method.

PHOTOCOPIABLE

Name:

Achievement

Keep the final **e** before a **suffix** beginning with a consonant, eg **hope + ful = hopeful**
Exceptions: **true + ly = truly, argue + ment = argument**

Drop the final **e** before a **suffix** beginning with a vowel, eg **live + ing = living**

- Fill in the **new word** column, making sure that you follow the rules.

Root	Suffix	New word
achieve	ment	achievement
advance	ing	
approve	al	
compare	able	
continue	ing	
courage	ous	
desire	able	
guide	ance	
hope	ful	
nine	ty	
retire	ment	
separate	ing	
severe	ly	
shame	less	
taste	ful	
true	ly	
tune	ful	
use	less	
whole	ly	

Dear Helper,

Objective: to learn spelling rules about words ending in e when adding a suffix.

Remind your child that a *suffix* is a group of letters added to the end of a word to change its meaning or use. Ask your child to read each word aloud and then look carefully at the suffix to see how to apply the two rules.

Beautiful

Words ending in consonant + **y**, change the **y** to **i** before adding any suffix not beginning with **i**, eg **friendly** + **er** = **friendlier**; **busy** + **ly** = **busily**.

- Fill in the **new word** column, making sure that you follow the rules.

friendly + er

friendlier

Root	Suffix	New word
beauty	ful	beautiful
busy	ly	
carry	er	
empty	ing	
friendly	est	
glory	fy	
happy	ness	
hungry	est	
lazy	ly	
marry	age	
mercy	less	
merry	est	
pity	ful	
pretty	ness	
reply	cate	
spy	ing	
supply	ed	
try	al	
vary	able	
windy	ly	

Dear Helper,

Objective: to learn spelling rule about words ending in y, when adding a suffix.

Remind your child that a *suffix* is a group of letters added to the end of a word to change its meaning or use. Ask your child to read each word aloud and then look carefully at the suffix to see how to apply the rule.

Except after c

Write **ie** when the sound is long **e** (**ee**) except after **c**, when you should write **ei**.

Examples: **chief, field, shield, ceiling, deceive, receive**
Exceptions: **either, height, leisure, neither, seize, their, weird**

Write **ei** when the sound is not long **e**, especially when the sound is long **a** (**ay**).

Examples: **eight, freight, height, neighbour, reign, weigh**
Exceptions: **friend, mischief**

- Add **ie** or **ei** in the gaps below.

th _ _ r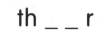

ach _ _ ve

bes _ _ ge

h _ _ ght

p _ _ rce

rel _ _ f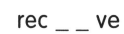

f _ _ rce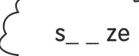

gr _ _ f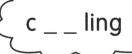

rec _ _ ve

s _ _ ze

c _ _ ling

w _ _ gh

_ _ ght

_ _ ther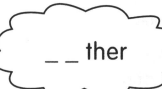

f _ _ ld

Extension

- Choose three of the words and use them in a sentence. You can write them on the back of this sheet.

Dear Helper,

Objective: to learn spelling rules about words containing ie or ei.

Help your child to write *ie* or *ei* in the gaps in the words above. If your child is not sure about any words, do not give the answer, but go over the rule and its exceptions and then ask your child to try again.

Verb to noun

Verbs (action words) can often be changed to nouns (naming words) by changing the endings.

- Choose endings from the list below to change the verbs in the first column into nouns. Note that you may need to adapt the spelling when adding the ending, eg **occupy – occupier.** The first one has been done for you.

al	**ar**	**er**	**or**	**tion**
ance	**ation**	**ment**	**y**	

Verb	Noun
act	actor
adopt	
advertise	
amuse	
appear	
approve	
attend	
attract	
beg	
begin	
civilise	
clean	
create	
discover	
invent	
learn	
occupy	
punish	
select	
teach	

Extension

- Choose three verbs and write pairs of sentences showing how they can be used as verbs and nouns. You can use the back of this sheet.

Dear Helper,

Objective: to change verbs to nouns.
Ask your child to read the words aloud, trying different endings until they find the one that sounds right. If in doubt, check in a dictionary.

PHOTOCOPIABLE

Noun to verb

Nouns (naming words) can often be changed to **verbs** (action words) by:

1   taking off an ending, eg **actor** – **act**;
2   adding an ending, eg **memory** – **memorise**;
3   changing the word, eg **blood** – **bleed**.

● Change the **nouns** in the first column into **verbs** and write them in the second column. In the last column, say how you made the change, using one of the numbers above. The first one has been done for you as an example.

Noun	Verb	How I made the change
actor	act	1
apology		
amazement		
blood		
circulation		
civilisation		
composition		
computer		
description		
economy		
education		
electricity		
magnet		
memory		
national		
obedience		
purity		
relief		
solution		
song		

Extension

● Choose three nouns and write pairs of sentences showing how they can be used as nouns and verbs. You can use the back of this sheet.

Dear Helper,

Objective: to change nouns to verbs.
Ask your child to read the words aloud, trying different endings until they find the one that sounds right. If in doubt, check in a dictionary.

Adjective to adverb

Adjectives (describing words) can often be changed to **adverbs** (words that describe verbs) by adding **–ly**. Note that, if the word ends in **y**, the **y** must be changed to **i**, eg hung**r**y, hung**ri**ly.

- Change the **adjectives** in the first column into **adverbs.** The first one has been done for you.

Adjective	Adverb
angry	angrily
anxious	
bad	
careful	
clumsy	
correct	
greedy	
happy	
hungry	
immediate	
quiet	
serious	
sudden	
sulky	
weak	

Extension

- Choose three adjectives and write pairs of sentences showing how they can be used as adjectives and adverbs. You can start below and continue on the back of this sheet.

Dear Helper,

Objective: to change adjectives to adverbs.

Ask your child to read the words aloud, then add the *–ly* ending, taking care with words ending in y.

From bad to worse

Sometimes we need to compare things: Zita is **tall**, but Rita is **taller**. Anita is the **tallest** of the three.

The **positive** is used to describe something, eg a **long** journey.

The **comparative** is used to compare two things, eg the journey to Rome was **longer** than the journey to London.

The **superlative** is used when comparing lots of things, eg the journey to the moon was the **longest** journey of all.

- Fill in the gaps in the boxes.

Positive	Comparative	Superlative
Regular with **–er**, **–est** endings		
fast	faster	fastest
small		smallest
	taller	
		thinnest
big		
Regular with **more** and **most**		
beautiful	more beautiful	most beautiful
comfortable		most comfortable
	more generous	
		most intelligent
handsome		
Irregular		
bad	worse	worst
		best
	less	
many		

Extension

- Choose a word from each of the boxes and write sentences for each, demonstrating the use of the **positive** form, the **comparative** form and the **superlative** form. You can use the back of this sheet.

Dear Helper,

Objective: to change adjectives to show degrees of comparison.

Encourage your child to say each degree of comparison before completing the table. Remind your child that *most* and *–est* should not be used together. They shouldn't, for example, say: *I am the most smartest.*

Linstead Market

Accent means variation in pronunciation.
Dialect means variation in vocabulary and grammar.

- Read the poem.
- Underline differences of **accent**.
- Highlight differences in **dialect**.
- Work out from the context what the dialect words mean.

Linstead Market

Carry me ackee go a Linstead market:
Not a quatty wut sell.
Carry me ackee go a Linstead market:
Not a quatty wut sell.
Chorus   Lard, wat a night, not a bite,
                    Wat a Satiday night.
                    Lard, wat night, not a bite,
                    Wat a Satiday night.

Everybody come feel up, feel up:
Not a quatty wut sell.
Everybody come feel up, squeeze up:
Not a quatty wut sell.
Chorus

Mek me call i' louder: ackee! ackee!
Red an pretty dem 'tan!
Lady, buy yu Sunday marnin brukfas',
Rice an ackee nyam gran'.
Chorus

All de pickney dem a linga, linga,
Fe weh dem mumma no bring.
All de pickney dem a linga, linga,
Fe weh dem mumma no bring.
Chorus

Traditional Caribbean

Dear Helper,

Objective: to understand how words vary across dialects.
Enjoy reading this poem aloud with your child (eg by sharing verses). Help your child to guess from the context what the dialect words might mean. They will be explained by the teacher back in the classroom.

W | Name:

American English

American English differs in some ways from British English. As it is the official language of a country, it is more appropriate to call it a **language variety** than a **dialect**.

● Complete this English–American dictionary by filling in the blanks. Add some more words if you know any.

English	American
	cookies
bonnet (of a car)	hood
boot (of a car)	
chemist	drugstore
	French fries
cinema	
cooker	stove
	chips
curtains	drapes
garden	yard
	vacation
ice box	refrigerator
	diaper
plaster	band aid
rubbish	
	sidewalk
	faucet
trousers	
	closet

Dear Helper,

Objective: to understand how words vary across dialects.
Have fun reading out the American words with an American accent! Most children will know the American equivalents, but may need help in a few places.

100 LITERACY HOMEWORK ACTIVITIES • YEAR 5 TERM 3

Name:

Hallucinate

Dictionaries contain a range of information about words. Here is a typical dictionary entry, followed by an explanation of the information it contains.

hallucinate (ha-loó-si-nate) *v.* false impressions
in the mind.   [*L. alucinari* wander in mind]

Spelling: the bold print word at the beginning of the entry shows the spelling.

Pronunciation: how a word should be pronounced, usually by re-spelling the word phonetically.

Part of speech: this is shown by abbreviations like the following:

noun *n.*	adjective *adj.*
verb *v.*	preposition *prep.*
adverb *adv.*	conjunction *conj.*

Meaning: this is the main purpose of the standard dictionary. Words with several meanings have long entries.

Etymology word origin: An abbreviation showing from which language the word comes. Common abbreviations are: *F.* French, *G.* Greek, *Ger.* German, *Goth.* Gothic, *L.* Latin, *ME.* Middle English, *ON.* Old Norse

- Find the answers to the following questions using your dictionary:

Is it correct to pronounce the **h** in **honour**?

What does the abbreviation **CBI** stand for?

What does **cosmos** mean?

From which language does **cosmos** originally come?

How many different meanings can you find for the word **bill**?

From which language does **skirt** originally come?

What is the meaning of the abbreviation **NATO**?

How should you pronounce the word **boatswain**?

Dear Helper,

Objective: to understand the different purposes of a dictionary.
Read through the explanation of a dictionary entry with your child, matching the features to those in the dictionary your child has brought home. Then, help to answer the questions.

Name:

Punctuation posers

A **comma** is used to mark off a **subordinate clause** when it begins the sentence.

Example:

main clause:
Cinderella changed back into a kitchen maid

subordinate clause:
When the clock struck twelve,

subordinate clause:
when the clock struck twelve.

main clause:
Cinderella changed back into a kitchen maid.

- Re-write these sentences putting the **subordinate clause** at the beginning and marking it off with a comma.

Tip: Find the **conjunction** and move it with the following clause to the beginning of the sentence.

Prince Charming was the favourite of the ladies because he was rich and handsome.

Buttons loved Cinderella although he was too shy to tell her.

The three sisters went to the ball while Cinderella cleaned out the fireplace.

Cinderella saw her fairy godmother when she looked up.

You will marry a prince even though you are poor.

Your coach will change back into a pumpkin unless you leave by midnight.

The three sisters were unkind to Cinderella because they were jealous of her.

I shall keep looking until I find the foot that fits this glass slipper.

Dear Helper,

Objective: **to use punctuation marks accurately in complex sentences.**

The hardest part of this homework is finding the subordinate clause. Find the conjunction, then move it with the following clause to the beginning of the sentence. This list of conjunctions will help you and your child: *although, because, though, unless, until, when, while.*

Name:

Name:

Punctuating Rapunzel

Commas are used like brackets to mark off a **phrase in apposition.** A phrase in apposition is a piece of extra information inserted into a sentence, eg

sentence: Rapunzel lived in a tower.
sentence + phrase in apposition: Rapunzel, a girl with very long hair, lived in a tower.

- Read these sentences. For each one, find the **phrase in apposition** and place a **comma** before and after it.

The tower a tall building without any steps was Rapunzel's home.

An old woman to whom the tower belonged kept her a prisoner.

She would shout her voice croaking cruelly 'Rapunzel, let down your hair!'

Rapunzel's hair like a long ladder hung down from the window.

The old woman who was more agile than she looked scrambled up Rapunzel's hair.

A handsome prince who was hiding nearby saw everything that happened.

Extension

- Write three sentences, each with a correctly punctuated phrase in apposition. You could write more about Rapunzel or choose another fairy tale. Use the back of this sheet.

Dear Helper,

Objective: to use punctuation marks accurately in complex sentences.
Go over the explanation, then ask your child to read each sentence aloud to you. Ask: *Which is the phrase of extra information? Try missing it out. Does the sentence still make sense?* After your child has added commas before and after the phrase, read the sentences again. It should be much easier now!

PHOTOCOPIABLE

Whose is it?

Apostrophes can be used with common and proper nouns to show possession.

Rule 1: If the noun is singular, add an **apostrophe** and an **s**.
Example: **John's gold, the teacher's pet, James's horse, the ass's tail.**

Rule 2: If the noun is plural and doesn't end in **s**, add an **apostrophe** and an **s**.
Example: **the children's toys, the men's waistcoats.**

Rule 3: If the noun is plural and ends in **s**, add an **apostrophe** but no **s**.
Example: **the smugglers' cave, the dogs' bones.**

- Rewrite these sentences using apostrophes.

The passengers ticket is no longer valid.

The headmistresss office door was firmly closed.

Janes socks do not match.

Mr Rosss class performed a nativity play in assembly.

The mices hole can be seen just by the front door.

I shivered when the doctors stethoscope touched my back.

Texass oil rigs dominate the landscape.

The womens race was won by an international athlete.

All the gardeners plants were ruined by the rain.

Dear Helper,

Objective: to revise use of the apostrophe to show possession.
Discuss how the use of apostrophes helps us to see what belongs to who. The last sentence is a tricky one.
Ask your child: *Is 'gardeners' singular or plural?*

All in a good clause (1)

A **main clause** makes sense on its own and contains a verb.
Example: Zoe **played** a tune on her saxophone.

A subordinate clause does not make sense on its own.
Example: A **difficult** piece of music

- Read each of these clauses and ask yourself:

   Does it contain a verb?
   Does it make sense on its own?

- Put a tick (✓) next to the **main clauses.**

The portrait was beautifully painted. ☐

A new and very powerful computer. ☐

I enjoy watching television. ☐

Spreading destruction everywhere. ☐

Chloe hoped to write a best selling novel. ☐

A difficult piece of homework. ☐

Taken completely by surprise. ☐

Tim enjoys playing snooker. ☐

By a strong wind. ☐

My new puppy made a mess on the carpet. ☐

Dear Helper,

Objective: to identify main clauses.
Remind your child that main clauses make sense on their own, but that subordinate clauses depend on main clauses for their sense.

Name:

All in a good clause (2)

Adjective clauses act like **adjectives**; they give more information about **nouns**. They are usually introduced by the following relative pronouns: **who, whom, whose, which, that.**

- Choose a **relative pronoun** from the list above to link the **nouns** and **adjective clauses** in the boxes below. The first one has been done for you.

Noun (in bold)	Relative pronoun	Adjective clause
This is the **programme**	that	I told you about.
Cabot is the **explorer**		discovered Newfoundland.
I wish to see the **boy**		football boots were left in the classroom.
Please upgrade the **computers**		are in the computer room.
This is for the **girl**		lost her history book.
It is different to the **school**		I went to last year.
The telescope is an **instrument**		makes it possible to see distant planets.
In the room there was a **girl**		was playing with a dog.
Kari was a new **pupil**		childhood had been spent in Kosovo.
Iceland is a **country**		is north of Scotland.

Dear Helper,

Objective: to investigate clauses by understanding how they are connected.

Though the terminology is difficult, the task is quite easy. Don't worry if your child doesn't immediately start to use the correct terminology. Ask your child to read the two clauses and try out different relative pronouns until they find one which sounds right.

Name:

All in a good clause (3)

Adverb clauses act like **adverbs**; they give more information about **how, when, where** or **why**. For example, the first adverb clause in the table explains **why** the band could not play. Adverb clauses are usually introduced by the following **subordinating conjunctions**: **after, although, as, because, before, unless, when, where, while.**

- Choose a **subordinating conjunction** from the list above to link the main clauses and adverb clauses. The first one has been done for you.

Main clause	Subordinating conjunction	Adverb clause (how, when, where, why)
The band couldn't play	because	Bill had forgotten his trombone.
We tuned up		Bill fetched his instrument.
We will not win the competition		we play our very best.
The recording sounded good		our drummer was sick.
We might even be famous		the CD is released.
We won't get into the top ten		swing music is not popular.
Don't forget to blow harder		the music should be loud.
We must tune up carefully		the concert starts.
There will be time to rest		the concert has finished.
I don't think I'll be a musician		it is too much like hard work.

Dear Helper,

Objective: to investigate clauses by understanding how they are connected.

Though the terminology is difficult, the task is quite easy. Don't worry if your child doesn't immediately start to use the correct terminology. Ask your child to read the two clauses and try out different subordinating conjunctions until they find one which sounds right. Sometimes, either of two conjunctions works equally well.

All in a good clause (4)

Noun clauses act like **nouns**. They are usually introduced by the following connectives: **that, whether, who, whoever, whose, where, why.**

- Choose suitable **relative pronouns** (connective) to link the **noun phrases** and **adjective clauses.** The first one has been done for you.

Main clause	Connective (relative pronoun)	Noun clause
Zoe could not remember	what	the homework was.
No one knows		broke the window.
My teacher taught		hard work brings success.
I do not know		suitcase that is.
A film has been made about		dinosaurs could be cloned.
The weather man was not sure		it would rain.
Do not let strangers in		they might be.
I can tell you		a good mechanic can be found.
The bill should be paid by		caused the accident.
Tim told the teacher		he couldn't do the work.

Dear Helper,

Objective: to investigate clauses by understanding how they are connected.

Though the terminology is difficult, the task is quite easy. Don't worry if your child doesn't immediately start to use the correct terminology. Ask your child to read the two clauses and try out different connectives until they find one which sounds right. Sometimes, either of two connectives works equally well.

Name: _____

Join it

Conjunctions are used to join different parts of a sentence together. Here are the ten most commonly used conjunctions:
although, and, as, because, but, for, until, when, where, while.

● Add an appropriate **conjunction** from the list above to join the clauses in each sentence.

He had completed his holiday plans _____ an unexpected problem arose.

There was a car in the garage _____ we couldn't use it because neither of us could drive.

People still talk about the haunting _____ it happened many years ago.

It was difficult to find the music shop _____ it was outside the main shopping centre.

Slowly the climber edged up the cliff _____ he managed to rescue the injured girl.

The weather was fine _____ we set out on our trip.

We stopped bailing out the water _____ it was just a waste of time.

Sunset Boulevard is the place _____ many stars have their homes.

Tom put up the tent _____ Jerry got the camping stove going.

The champion started running at dawn _____ she didn't stop until she had beaten her record.

Dear Helper,

Objective: to use conjunctions to join clauses.
Ask your child to read each sentence aloud and try different conjunctions until they find one that sounds right. More than one may be appropriate.

The Rain-Making Ceremony

For the Lango people of Uganda, rain is a matter of life and death.
Every year, they perform this ceremony to make sure that the rains come.

- Read 'The Rain-Making Ceremony', but
  be careful – if you read it too well, it might work!

Verse	Response
We overcome this wind.	We overcome.
We desire the rain to fall, that it be poured in showers quickly.	Be poured.
Ah! rain, I beg you to fall. If you rain, it is good.	It is good.
A drizzling confusion.	Confusion.
If it rains and our food ripens, it is good.	It is good
If the children rejoice, it is good.	It is good.
If it rains, it is good. If our women rejoice, it is good.	It is good.
If the young men sing, it is good.	It is good.
A drizzling confusion.	Confusion.
If our grain ripens, it is good.	It is good.
If our women rejoice.	It is good.
If the children rejoice.	It is good.
If the young men sing.	It is good.
If the aged rejoice.	It is good.
An overflowing in the granary.	Overflowing.
May our grain fill the granaries.	May it fill.
A torrent in flow.	A torrent.
If the wind veers to the south, it is good.	It is good.
If the rain veers to the south, it is good.	It is good.
Ah! rain, I beg you to fall.	Fall! Fall!

The Lango People, Uganda

- Discuss why rain is so important to the Lango people.

Dear Helper,

Objective: to read a text from a different culture.
Share the reading of this ceremony with your child. Take it in turns to read the verse and response. Think of actions to go with the ceremony. Discuss the importance of rain to the Lango people.

Tramp trouble

● Read this passage which is written from the viewpoint of Bill, who is a tramp.

Bill tried the iron ring on the church door. It turned and the door opened. He sighed with relief. He could sleep snug tonight. Life was getting harder for gentlemen of the road – he didn't like to think of himself as a tramp. Farmers locked their barns, vicars locked their churches – there was no trust these days.

    Bill groped his way around the darkened church looking for a good place to sleep. Eventually he settled himself in the choir stalls in the chancel. He took a grubby grey blanket from a plastic bag and spread it over himself. Within minutes he was sound asleep.

    Suddenly, he was awoken by the sound of the church door creaking open. 'Oh dear,' he thought. 'What if it is the vicar – still, if it is, perhaps he'll give me a bowl of soup and let me stay here.'

    Then he heard the sound of children's voices. Bill hated children because they sometimes teased him or threw things at him. He wondered how he could get rid of them. Should he pretend to be the vicar and order them out, or should he hide and wait for them to go?

    'I don't like it,' wailed one voice, 'it's dark and creepy!'

    'Course it's creepy!' said another. 'What do you expect on a ghost hunt?'

    That gave Bill an idea. He took his old grey blanket and put it round his head so that he looked like the ghost of a monk. Then he started to make a low moaning sound...

● Now, re-write the passage from the viewpoint of the children. You can use the back of this sheet.
  • Decide how many children there are. Give them names.
  • What do they do when they hear the moaning?
  • What do they do when they see what looks like the ghost of a monk?

Dear Helper,

Objective: to retell a story from a different point of view.
Share the reading of the story with your child. Talk about what it must have been like from the children's point of view. This will provide a good foundation for the child's writing.

PHOTOCOPIABLE

Anecdotes

An **anecdote** is a short, interesting and sometimes amusing story. Anecdotes are usually true stories.

- Read this **anecdote** and then re-write it from Robert's point of view. Use a separate sheet.

When I was a lad, my best friend was called Robert. We used to enjoy playing in an old brickyard. It was a dangerous place – but well, lads are not as careful as they should be! One day, we found a huge rock which was propped up on some smaller rocks so that it looked like a table – 'Table Rock' we called it. We made a den undernearth, and got some old things from the local rubbish tip – chairs with broken springs, boxes and so on. We made a really comfortable den, I can tell you. Home from home it was!

Well, one day, Robert said that he'd had a row with his mum, and that he'd run away from home and was going to live under Table Rock. I stayed with him till teatime, then I had to go home. I promised him I'd bring him some food later. Well, when I got home, a great storm started – thunder and lightening – torrents of rain. I thought of poor old Robert under 'Table Rock' and felt a bit sorry for him.

After tea, the storm stopped, and I went to the brickyard. Guess what I found! The storm had caused an avalanche. The rocks had moved, and 'Table Rock' had fallen flat. I shouted for Robert, but it was no good; he must have been squashed as flat as a pancake. I cried all the way home. When I got in my mum said, 'Where've you been? Here's Robert waiting for you!' I couldn't believe my eyes.

When I asked him what happened, he said that he got so hungry, he decided to forgive his mum and go home for tea. And a good thing, too – his appetite saved his life!

Dear Helper,

Objective: to change point of view.
Rather than use the anecdote on the sheet, you may like to tell your child a memory or anecdote of your own, for them to change into a story.

The Mummers' play

Mummers' plays developed from oral story-telling and were one of the earliest forms of performance plays. They are simple plays about good and evil and life and death. They were often performed at ceremonies to hasten the end of winter and cheer on the spring.

- Read this scene and prepare it for performance. Concentrate on speaking the lines realistically. Memorise your part if you can. Think about how you would present it on stage.

Presenter: I open the door, I enter in;
I hope your favour we shall win.
Stir up the fire and strike a light,
And see my merry boys act to-night.
Whether we stand or whether we fall,
We'll do our best to please you all.

[Enter the actors.]

Presenter: Room, room, brave gallants all,
Pray give us room to rhyme;
We're come to show activity,
This merry Christmas time;
Activity of youth,
Activity of age,
The like was never seen
Upon a common stage.
And if you don't believe what I say,
Step in St George – and clear the way.

[St George steps forward.]

St George: In come I, St George,
The man of courage bold;
With my broad axe and sword
I won a crown of gold.
I fought the fiery dragon,
And drove him to the slaughter,
And by these means I won
The King of Egypt's daughter.
Show me the man that bids me stand;
I'll cut him down with my courageous hand.

Presenter: Step in, Bold Slasher.

[Bold Slasher steps forward.]

Slasher: In come I, the Turkish Knight,
Come from the Turkish land to fight.
I come to fight St George,
The man of courage bold;
And if his blood be hot,
I soon will make it cold.

St George: Stand off, stand off, Bold Slasher,
And let no more be said,
For if I draw my sword,
I'm sure to break thy head.
Thou speakest very bold,
To such a man as I;
I'll cut thee into eyelet holes,
And make thy buttons fly.

Slasher: My head is made of iron,
My body is made of steel,
My arms and legs of beaten brass;
No man can make me feel.

St George: Then draw thy sword and fight,
Or draw thy purse and pay;
For satisfaction I must have,
Before I go away.

Slasher: No satisfaction shalt thou have,
But I will bring thee to thy grave.

St George: Battle to battle with thee I call,
To see who on this ground shall fall.

Slasher: Battle to battle with thee I pray,
To see who on this ground shall lay.

St George: Then guard thy body and thy mind,
Or else my sword shall strike thee dead.

Slasher: One shall die and the other shall live;
This is the challenge that I do give.

[They fight. Slasher falls.]

Dear Helper,

Objective: to read, rehearse and perform poetry.

Read this poetic play with your child, then help them to prepare for a performance, eg by learning one of the parts and thinking about how it might be staged.

Phantom of Delight

This is one of several poems written by William Wordsworth about a woman called Lucy.

- Read the poem, then highlight all the words and phrases describing Lucy.
  Use different coloured pens to highlight **metaphors** and **similes** about Lucy.

SHE was a phantom of delight
When first she gleamed upon my sight;
A lovely apparition, sent
To be a moment's ornament;
Her eyes as stars of twilight fair;
Like twilight's too, her dusky hair;
But all things else about her drawn
From May-time and the cheerful dawn;
A dancing shape, an image gay,
To haunt, to startle, and waylay.

I saw her upon nearer view,
A spirit, yet a woman too!
Her household motions light and free,
And steps of virgin liberty;
A countenance in which did meet
Sweet records, promises as sweet;
A creature not too bright or good
For human nature's daily food;
For transient sorrows, simple wiles,
Praise, blame, love, kisses, tears, and smiles.

And now I see with eye serene.
The very pulse of the machine;
A being breathing thoughtful breath,
A traveller between life and death;
The reason firm, the temperate will,
Endurance, foresight, strength, and skill;
A perfect woman, nobly planned,
To warn, to comfort, and command;
And yet a spirit still, and bright
With something of angelic light.

William Wordsworth, 1798

- Write a short character sketch of Lucy. Use the back of this sheet.

Dear Helper,

Objective: to explore the appeal of older literature.
Share the reading of this poem with your child, or read it to them. Take some time to investigate the meaning of the more difficult words, eg *transient*. If there is dictionary available, encourage your child to use it..

Name:

The Secret Garden

This is the opening to the famous novel, *The Secret Garden*, written in 1911.

- Read the extract aloud. Note the punctuation – the sentences are very long!
- Underline all the words and phrases that describe Mary.

When Mary Lennox was sent to Misselthwaite Manor to live with her uncle, everybody said she was the most disagreeable-looking child ever seen. It was true, too. She had a little thin face and a little thin body, thin light hair and a sour expression. Her hair was yellow, and her face was yellow because she had been born in India and had always been ill in one way or another. Her father had held a position under the English Government and had always been busy and ill himself, and her mother had been a great beauty who cared only to go to parties and amuse herself with carefree people. She had not wanted a little girl at all, and when Mary was born she handed her over to the care of an Ayah*, who was made to understand that if she wished to please the Memsahib** she must keep the child out of sight as much as possible. So, when she was a sickly, fretful, ugly little baby she was kept out of the way, and when she became a sickly, fretful, toddling thing she was kept out of the way also. She never remembered seeing familiarly anything but the dark faces of her Ayah and the other native servants, and as they always obeyed her and gave her her own way in everything, because the Memsahib would be angry if she was disturbed by her crying, by the time she was six years old she was as tyrannical and selfish a little pig as ever lived.

Frances Hodgson Burnett

*Ayah = servant; nanny **Memsahib = mistress of the house*

Extension

- The last sentence is made up of many clauses. Re-write the sentence as three separate sentences. Use the back of this sheet.

Dear Helper,

Objective: to explore older literature, eg extracts from classic serials.

Read this extract with your child. The vocabulary is not difficult, but the sentence construction is challenging. Encourage your child to take heed of the punctuation. Discuss the description of Mary: *Does it give a good mental picture of what the girl was like?* If your child does the extension activity, help them to find the three sentences in one.

Shakespeare's language

Julius Caesar was written in 1597 by William Shakespeare. It tells the story of the first Roman emperor, who was assassinated by Brutus. In this scene, Caesar's wife, Calpurnia, tries to stop Caesar going out to the Senate because she has seen and heard about some frightening signs.

- Read this scene aloud.
- Re-write the scene in simple modern English using the glossary to help you. Use a separate sheet.

	Glossary
Calpurnia:	
Caesar, I never *stood on ceremonies*,	believed in signs
Yet now they *fright* me. There is *one within*,	frighten, someone inside
Besides the things that we have heard and seen,	
Recounts most *horrid* sights seen by the *watch*.	tells of, horrible, guards
A lioness hath *whelped* in the streets;	given birth
And graves have yawned, and *yielded* up their dead;	given
Fierce fiery warriors fought upon the clouds,	
In ranks and squadrons *and right form of* war,	just like a real
Which drizzled blood upon the Capitol;	
The noise of battle hurtled in the air,	
Horses *did neigh*, and dying men *did groan*,	neighed, groaned
And ghosts *did shriek* and squeal about the streets.	shrieked
O Caesar! These things are *beyond all use*,	not normal
And I do fear them.	
Caesar:	
What can be avoided	
Whose end is *purposed* by the mighty gods?	intended
Yet Caesar shall go *forth*; for these predictions	out
Are *to the world in general* as to Caesar.	for everybody
Calpurnia:	
When beggars die, there are no comets seen;	
The heavens themselves blaze forth the death of princes.	
Caesar:	
Cowards die many times before their deaths;	
The *valiant* never taste of death but once.	brave

Dear Helper,

Objective: to explore the challenge and appeal of older literature.

Read this scene a number of times with your child, taking different parts each time. On one of the readings, substitute the words in the glossary for those in italics.

Name:

Desert island

- Read this extract from the beginning of *Robinson Crusoe* by Daniel Defoe (published in 1719).
- Write a continuation describing how the ship sinks and Robinson Crusoe manages to get to an island and survive. Do not try to follow the original story – use your own ideas. Write in the same style, using the first person 'I' and make the language sound 'old fashioned'. Write your story on the back of this sheet.

By this time it blew a terrible storm indeed, and now I began to see terror and amazement in the faces even of the seamen themselves. The master, though vigilant in the business of preserving the ship, yet as he went in and out of his cabin by me, I could hear him softly to himself say several times, 'Lord, be merciful to us, we shall be all lost, we shall be all undone'; and the like.

During these first hurries, I was stupid, lying still in my cabin, which was in the steerage, and cannot describe my temper. I could ill reassume the first penitence which I had so apparently trampled upon, and hardened myself against. I thought the bitterness of death had been past, and that this would be nothing too, like the first. But when the master himself came by me, as I said just now, and said we should be all lost, I was dreadfully frighted. I got up out of my cabin and looked out; but such a dismal sight I never saw. The sea went mountains high, and broke upon us every three or four minutes.

When I could look about, I could see nothing but distress round us: Two ships that rid near us, we found, had cut their masts by the board, being deep loaden; and our men cried out that a ship which rid about a mile ahead of us was foundered. Two more ships, being driven from their anchors, were run out of the roads to sea at all adventures, and that with not a mast standing.

Dear Helper,

Objective: to write in the style of a given author.

Read this extract with your child. Don't worry about understanding all the archaic language. It is the gist of the story and a general feeling for the old-fashioned style that is important for the activity. Discuss what might happen on the island – make up new adventures. Talk about how to write the continuation using Defoe's style.

Name:

My Dad, Your Dad

- Read this dialogue poem aloud. It would be best to read it with someone else, but you could also read it by yourself, using two different voices.

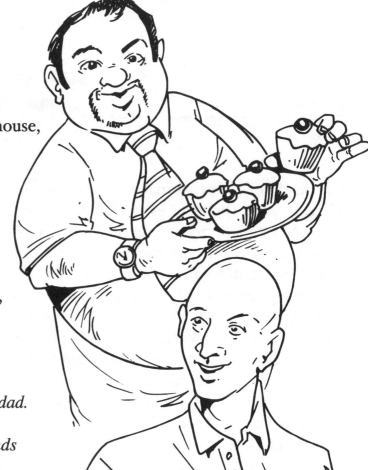

My Dad, Your Dad
My dad's fatter than your dad,
Yes, my dad's fatter than yours:
If he eats any more he won't fit in the house,
He'll have to live out of doors.

Yes, but my dad's balder than your dad,
Yes, my dad's balder, O.K.,
He's only got two hairs left on his head
And both are turning grey.

Ah, but my dad's thicker than your dad,
My dad's thicker, alright.
He has to look at his watch to see
If it's noon or the middle of the night.

Yes, but my dad's more boring than your dad.
If he ever starts counting sheep
When he can't get to sleep at night, he finds
It's the sheep that go to sleep.

But my dad doesn't mind your dad.
Mine quite likes yours too.
I suppose *they* don't always think much of US!
That's true, I suppose, that's true.

Kit Wright

- Write your own dialogue poem based on an everyday conversation. It doesn't have to rhyme. Prepare it for performance.

Dear Helper,

Objective: to use a performance poem as a model for own writing.
Read the poem with your child, each taking a part. Encourage as much expression as possible. Discuss what everyday conversation might be used to write a similar poem. Improvise the conversation to help with the writing.

Old school fields

In his letter below, Mr Rudge is understandably upset that new houses are going to be built nearby, but his letter of complaint is full of **bias, hearsay** and **deliberate misrepresentations of fact.**

- Use different coloured pens to highlight all the examples of these that you can find in the letter.
- Write a reply to Mr Rudge from the council's point of view. Use a separate piece of paper.

Dear Sir,

I am writing to protest about the plans for the new dwelling units in Old School Fields. Ten houses are far too many for such a tiny field. There will be terrible problems with road access. As you can see from the plan, the road will be very narrow. This will mean that it will be congested with traffic, and this will cause many accidents. It will be the children who suffer most.

A friend of mine, who is a builder, says that there is no main drain anywhere near the Old School Field, and that these houses will have to have cess tanks. That will cause a terrrible smell in summer, and my wife suffers from hay fever.

Another thing is that the old school will be knocked down. The keystone over the front door says 1881. Surely this is a historic building which should be preserved? I think this is just another example of profiteering by builders. They want to knock it down so that they can squeeze in another two houses.

Also, I have heard a rumour that these houses will be used to accommodate people who have caused problems on other estates. This is a nice quiet area and we can do without those kinds of problems. If these plans go ahead, it will ruin our quality of life.

Yours faithfully,

Mr Ivor G. Rudge

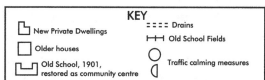

KEY

New Private Dwellings   Drains

Older houses   Old School Fields

Old School, 1901, restored as community centre   Traffic calming measures

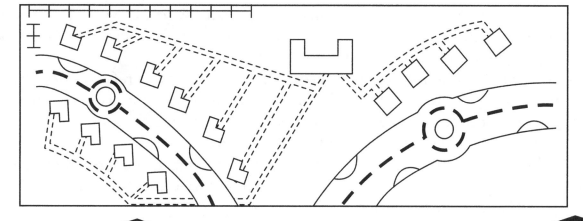

Dear Helper,

Objective: to recognise bias.

Help your child to compare the opinions stated in the letter with the facts shown on the plan. Discuss how a council official from the planning department might reply.

PHOTOCOPIABLE

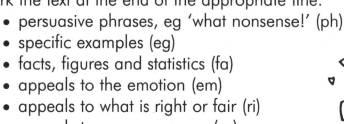

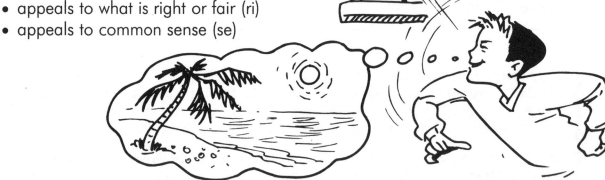

One kid crime wave

- Find the **persuasive devices** used in this article. Use the code in brackets to mark the text at the end of the appropriate line:
    - persuasive phrases, eg 'what nonsense!' (ph)
    - specific examples (eg)
    - facts, figures and statistics (fa)
    - appeals to the emotion (em)
    - appeals to what is right or fair (ri)
    - appeals to common sense (se)

Young offenders need to be dealt with more severely, otherwise they will continue to break the law, and end up living a life of crime.

An example is Ben (his real name has been changed). Local people have nicknamed him the 'one kid crime wave'. In the year before his arrest last September he had committed 20 crimes. These included burglary, blackmail, attacking an old age pensioner and various motor vehicle offences. Yet he was let off with a caution, or let out on bail every time he was caught.

Social workers tried to solve Ben's problems by sending him on a two-week holiday to St Lucia, an island in the Caribbean. They say that this will help to improve his self-confidence, and set him on the right track to becoming a law-abiding citizen. How unfair! Just imagine how that poor old age pensioner must have felt when he heard that Ben had been sent to the Caribbean!

No one but a complete idiot would believe that this could work. It is rewarding Ben for his crimes. Now he will think that, the next time he fancies an exotic holiday, all he has to do is hit an old lady over the head!

Every right-thinking person can see that the only way to reform boys like Ben is to punish them for their crimes. If Ben had been punished for his first crime, for example, by being sent to a young offenders secure unit for a few months, then perhaps the other 19 crimes would not have been committed.

This is the common sense way of dealing with young offenders which the vast majority of people support – and these are the people who pay, through taxes, for an effective system of law and order.

Dear Helper,

Objective: to investigate the use of persuasive devices.

Read the passage with your child, then help them to find the persuasive techniques used in the passage. Discuss the issue and offer your own opinions. If time allows, do the same with an article in the newspaper.

Name:

Book advertisement

- Prepare an advertisement for a book using these headings

Title and Author (Give full details.)

Illustration (Draw your own sketch to give the reader an idea of what the book is about. Do not copy the book's cover, but think of your own idea.)

Main character (Describe what he or she is like, and what he or she does.)

Main character (Draw a simple sketch of the main character.)

Outline of story (Give an outline of the story that would interest the reader. However, be careful not to give away the ending.)

Dear Helper,

Objective: to persuade someone to buy a book through an advertisement.
Talk about the book that your child has chosen to advertise. Discuss what he or she will write or draw.

Boreham supertram

- Read the letter from Boreham Council.
- Discuss the good and bad points of the plan.

Boreham Town Hall
Boreham
BT3 TCH

4 January 2001

Residents of Boreham
All residential addresses

Dear Resident,

Boreham Council is pleased to announce plans for a modern tramway
system which will be fast, economical and environmentally-friendly. A
plan of the tramway system is given below. When the tramway is
completed, all cars will be banned from the town centre, and must be
left at the 'Supertram Parks' outside the town. Fares will be between
£2 and £5 depending on the length of the journey. If you would like to
send us your views about the plans, please write to me within thirty
days at the address in the top right-hand corner.

Yours sincerely,

Mr Leclerk
On behalf of Boreham Council

KEY

═══ B roads

─── A roads

- - - Proposed route of Supertram

╫╫╫ Railway track (disused)

P Park and ride

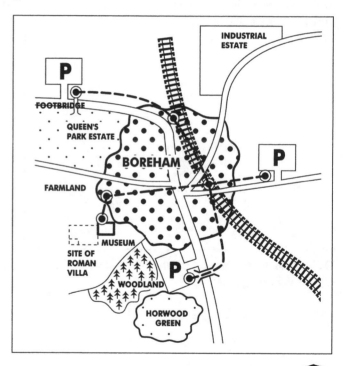

- Write a letter supporting or arguing against the plan, following the letter template.
  Use a separate sheet.

Dear Helper,

Objective: to write a letter expressing a point of view.

If there is a local issue that your child could write about, use it instead of the Boreham Supertram. Ensure that
your child fully understands the issue, eg by reading a newspaper article, or by explaining it yourself. Write
about the issue on another sheet of paper, following the template provided.

Uniform arguments

- Read the notes **For** school uniform, then in the space below, make notes **Against** school uniform.

For

Makes children look smart.

People can tell which school you belong to.

School should not be seen as a fashion show.

Helps children develop pride in their appearance.

Improves discipline.

Stops rich children from showing off by wearing a different outfit each day.

Cheaper for parents.

Against

Dear Helper,

Objective: to construct an argument in note form.

Read through the statements for school uniform with your child, then hold a discussion about the issue. This will help to give your child ideas for arguments against school uniforms.

Year 5 Homework Diary

Name _____

Name of activity	Date sent home	Child's comments		Helper's comments	Teacher's comments
		Did you like this? ☑ Tick a face. ☺ a lot 😐 a little ☹ not much	**Write some comments on what you learned.**		
		☺ a lot 😐 a little ☹ not much			
		☺ a lot 😐 a little ☹ not much			
		☺ a lot 😐 a little ☹ not much			